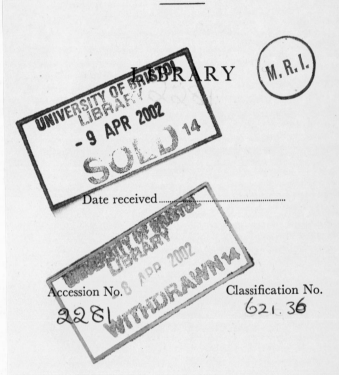

INDUCTION AND DIELECTRIC HEATING

' Heating with machine-tool precision '

ELECTRICITY AND PRODUCTIVITY SERIES
No. 6

Induction and Dielectric Heating

BRITISH ELECTRICAL DEVELOPMENT ASSOCIATION

ELECTRICITY AND PRODUCTIVITY

This book is one of a series dealing with specialised
industrial applications of electricity. The titles of
the first eight books are given below

Publication dates and further information
can be obtained by application to:

THE DIRECTOR AND SECRETARY

BRITISH ELECTRICAL DEVELOPMENT ASSOCIATION

2 SAVOY HILL, LONDON, W.C.2

TELEPHONE: TEMPLE BAR 9434

Preface

QUITE early in the history of electricity two discoveries were made. Experimenters found that when a conductor carrying an alternating current of electricity surrounded a core of magnetic material, it caused the material to get hot. They also found that heat was produced in electrical insulators when subjected to the forces of an alternating field.

Later, when alternating currents became a factor in the industrial and commercial development of electric power, designers of electrical equipment had to allow for these phenomena which caused unwanted but unavoidable losses of energy.

Today practical knowledge of the effects of these phenomena has formed the basis of new heating processes—processes by which heat may be imparted to a given object in definite and controllable amounts just where and how it is wanted.

It is spectacular to witness a bar of steel becoming incandescent when inserted in a water cooled copper coil; to see the transformation of metal into liquid and all this within the confines of a wooden box, and to observe a mass of non-conducting material become hot, all without a visible source of heat.

The object of this book is to give to the reader a new line of approach to the ever increasing number of heating problems which modern needs have brought into the realms of metallurgy, chemistry and physics, and to help him apply effectively the new methods which electricity has offered.

Problems of heat transfer are still with us, as they were with the early potters of clay. It is true we have today instruments to measure and control temperature, new insulating materials to conserve heat, fans and other devices to assist the circulation of furnace atmospheres, but none of these give the quantitative control of heat without which no heating process can be determined with mathematical accuracy.

The potter relied upon craftsmanship and even today the quality of a heated product depends largely upon skill and experience; but induction and dielectric heating—the newer methods of generating heat—eliminate many of the problems. Skill and experience become less essential, and a uniformly better product is obtained.

It is shown how vital a part electricity plays in a wide range of new processes; how, with the aid of dielectric heating new uses of synthetic materials have revolutionised the conception and design of many articles of everyday use; and how the adoption of well chosen applications of induction heating or dielectric heating ameliorates factory conditions, improves the product, and increases productivity.

Acknowledgements

The British Electrical Development Association acknowledge with thanks the assistance and photographs received from the following: Bakelite Ltd., Beanwy Electric Ltd., Blakey's Boot Protectors Ltd., British Industrial Plastics Ltd., Birlec Ltd., Delapena Ltd., Electric Furnace Co. Ltd., English Electric Co. Ltd., Expert Tool Heat Treatments Ltd., Ford Motor Co. Ltd., General Electric Co. Ltd., Isopad Ltd., Kestner Evaporator & Engineering Co. Ltd., Metalectric Furnaces Ltd., Metropolitan-Vickers Electrical Co. Ltd., Philips Electrical Ltd., Pye Ltd., Radio Heaters Ltd., Redifon Ltd., Vauxhall Motors Ltd., Wild-Barfield Electric Furnaces Ltd., G. L. Willan Ltd.

Contents

PART ONE

CHAPTER I. INDUCTION MELTING OF METALS

PART TWO

CHAPTER 2. INDUCTION HEATING
FOR METALLURGICAL PURPOSES

Illustrations

xiii

TABLES

Introduction

THE VALUE OF INDUCTION AND DIELECTRIC HEATING TO INDUSTRY

Induction and dielectric heating are basically different from all other forms of heating. Unlike other methods in which heat is transferred by convection, conduction, or radiation from an external heat source to the work, electrical energy is applied in a manner which causes heat to be generated in the substance itself.

The amount of energy converted to heat can be controlled accurately, and definite quantities may be generated within the substance to produce heat where it is required. There is no problem of getting the heat to flow into the work as with other methods, and the rate of heating can be many times faster.

The processes of induction and dielectric heating when appropriately applied, enable things to be made better, quicker and cheaper. Working conditions are improved because there is no external heating source which dissipates heat to the surroundings.

The productive capacity of a unit of floor space can be increased many times and skilled labour becomes unnecessary. Many heating applications previously regarded as impracticable may become possible and poor heat conducting materials may be treated quickly and continuously.

BASIC DESCRIPTION OF THE PHENOMENA OF INDUCTION AND DIELECTRIC HEATING

(a) *Electro-magnetic induction heating of metals and other electrical conductors.*

When any material which is capable of conducting electric current is placed within the magnetic field set up by a conductor carrying an alternating current, eddy currents are induced in the material, causing it to become hot. The eddy currents are themselves alternating and have the property common to all alternating currents of flowing with their greatest density at the surface of the metal.

The induced heating effect, is therefore, most intense at the surface of the material, but if the current is maintained for an appreciable time heat will be conducted towards the centre. Should the heating be continued the material will be heated right through,

A

and if the current is of sufficient magnitude and maintained for sufficient time, the material will melt.

Early in the nineteenth century the phenomenon of induction heating was applied to the experimental melting of metals.

The earlier furnaces consisted of a circular hearth or trough which contained the molten metal in the form of an annular ring. This formed a short circuited single-turn secondary winding of a transformer which was energised by a supply of alternating current at normal frequency. The design had inherent defects. Mechanical forces set up by the current flowing in the molten metal tended to cause it to contract locally and could result in the interruption of the current with resultant operating difficulties. Many attempts were made to solve the 'pinch effect', as it was called, but it was not until the early 1900's that Wyatt removed the difficulty by placing the secondary channel in the vertical plane. The weight of metal in the bath was then sufficient to overcome the forces which were the cause of the pinch effect. A new approach was made later by Dr. E. F. Northrup, who substituted a crucible containing the metal, in place of the channel and surrounded it with a multi-turn coil through which current was passed at high frequency.

The development of these two types of induction melting furnaces—the former for brass and the latter for steel—was extremely rapid, and many hundreds of thousands of kWs of capacity are installed throughout the World today.

It was not, however, until about 1935 that any further serious attempt was made to apply induction heating for industrial purposes. Then a process was developed for the surface hardening of crankshaft journals.

Subsequently the principle was applied to the surface hardening of other components and to the heating of parts for other purposes.

Electro-magnetic or eddy-current heating of metals occurs at all frequencies. Normal mains frequency is used extensively for the induction melting of non-ferrous metals and today the heating of non-ferrous billets for extrusion or rolling, by normal frequency, is finding increasing favour.

Generally, however, frequencies ranging from 300 cycles per second up to 1,000,000 cycles per second are necessary for most applications in the metallurgical field.

Suitable apparatus must, therefore, be used to provide the high frequency source of energy for this purpose. Four types of generators have been developed:

2

1. Rotating equipment consisting of a high frequency generator driven by a normal electric motor.
2. Electronic valve generator.
3. Spark-gap generator.
4. Mercury arc frequency changer.

Of these the rotating equipment and valve generator are in general use for the melting of metals and for heat treatment purposes, the spark-gap oscillator being restricted mainly to the melting of small quantities of special metals.

The mercury arc, applied as a frequency changer for industrial power purposes is a newer development, useful so far, for the melting of metals at a frequency of about 2,000 cycles per second.

(b) *Dielectric heating of non-metals*

The second phenomenon relates to the heating of electrical non-conducting substances or insulators, which are generally, by their nature, also poor conductors of heat.

When such a substance is placed between two metal plates called electrodes across which an alternating voltage is applied, the material undergoes molecular disturbance, as a result of which it is heated.

The phenomenon occurs at all frequencies but for industrial heating purposes frequencies of some millions of cycles per second are necessary. The electronic valve provides a means of obtaining a suitable supply, and following upon the rapid development of high powered radio transmitting valves, generators of adequate capacity and frequency are now available for all industrial applications.

CONSUMPTION OF ELECTRICITY

Some loss of power occurs when converting commercial mains frequency to high frequency; the loss varies according to the method of conversion, and the size of the generator. It is logical to relate the energy absorbed by the work to that taken from the high frequency source of power, because the efficiency of induction heating and dielectric heating concerns the effective use of high frequency electricity and not the efficiency of raising the frequency of the normal power supply. The thermal efficiency of high frequency heating is represented by

$$\frac{\text{Heat absorbed by the work}}{\text{Heat equivalent of power taken from the high frequency source}}$$

It should be remembered, therefore, that when power consumption figures are quoted, these relate to power taken from the output

3

terminals of the high frequency generator and not to power drawn from the electricity mains at commercial frequency.

NOMENCLATURE FOR HIGH FREQUENCY INDUCTION AND DIELECTRIC HEATING (*cf. Glossary*)

The general term 'high frequency' (abbreviated H.F.) is used to denote any frequency higher than that at which a public supply can be obtained, but a restricted use is made of 'radio frequency' (abbreviated R.F.) to designate those frequencies above about 25,000 cycles per second.

INDUCTION AND DIELECTRIC HEATING

Induction and dielectric heating are analagous in many characteristics, but there are fundamental differences between them and each has a distinct field of application. Further, induction heating may be subdivided between heating for melting and heating for heat-treatment purposes.

The subjects of induction and dielectric heating are therefore dealt with in three parts, each complete in itself.

Part I. Induction melting of metals.

Part II. Induction heating for metal heat-treatment.

Part III. Dielectric heating.

Frequency conversion and generator design are subjects of vital importance to the manufacturer of induction heating equipment, but the potential user is naturally more interested in the industrial purposes for which such equipment may be used, the heating problems involved and the economics of manufacture. More stress is laid, therefore, upon the application of induction and dielectric heating than upon selection of frequencies and methods of generation.

Will high frequency methods—

Improve the quality and consistency of the product ?

Reduce manufacturing costs ?

Increase productivity ?

An examination of the more important industrial applications will enable these questions to be answered.

4

PART ONE

I

Induction melting of metals

1.1 INTRODUCTION

The oldest and largest application of induction heating lies in the melting of metals. Normal frequency, high frequency and radio frequency furnaces have been developed, but fundamentally, all types of induction melting furnaces are similar.

Representative core-types are illustrated diagrammatically in Figures 1, 4, 5, and 7. Each type comprises an inductor coil, a refractory lining or crucible, and an iron core to concentrate the magnetic field. The coreless type (Figure 7) comprises an inductor coil and a refractory lining only. As the name infers an iron core is unnecessary.

The inductor coil is fed with alternating current at the requisite voltage, and the electro-magnetic field set up passes through either a part, or the whole of the furnace charge, which acts in effect as a short-circuited secondary winding of a transformer, carrying a heavy induced current.

The induced current generates heat within the furnace charge by resistance heating, and when the current is of sufficient magnitude and maintained for a sufficient time, the metal melts. Melting occurs therefore without the agency of external heat.

1.2 ADVANTAGES OF INDUCTION MELTING

The primary assets of induction melting are:

1. Freedom from deleterious gases and products of combustion, which can cause undesirable metallurgical re-actions such as oxidation, de-oxidation and sulphur contamination.

2. Rapid speed of melting.

Relative to size induction melting furnaces have a larger daily production than other types of furnaces.

Secondary but important considerations are:

3. Low running costs.

4. Improved working conditions.

There are no discomforts from excessive dissipation of heat from the furnace, no smoke, no dirt, and no ashes to be removed.

5. Reduced metal loss.

When melting copper/zinc alloys, the loss of zinc by oxidation may be less than $\frac{1}{2}$ of 1 per cent of its weight.

6. Automatic stirring.

Powerful stirring forces occur within the molten metal ensuring adequate mixing to give homogeneous composition, and enable consistent and accurate alloy specifications to be met.

7. Low maintenance cost of the refractory linings.

No part of the furnace becomes hotter than the metal itself.

1.3 NORMAL FREQUENCY CORE-TYPE INDUCTION MELTING FURNACE

The furnace illustrated at Figure 1 is most suitable for the continuous production of one class of alloy and is used mainly for melting brass, nickel, silver, and zinc. Furnace capacity capable of an annual output of over 1,000,000 tons of brass has already been installed in the United Kingdom.

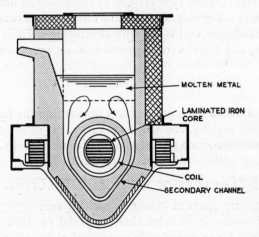

Fig. 1. Wyatt core-type induction furnace.

This furnace is still widely referred to by its original name, 'Ajax-Wyatt', after the inventor Wyatt and the original makers Ajax Manufacturing Company of U.S.A., but is more technically known as the 'submerged resistor' induction furnace because the effective part of the furnace in which the heat is generated is below the main body of molten metal. It takes the form of a loop of molten metal in a vertical, refractory lined channel, the top ends of which communicate with the main body of the metal. The body of the melt and the channel form the secondary of a transformer, the channel being proportioned to give a suitably high resistance with the particular metal which has to be melted.

Fig. 2. An installation of Wyatt furnaces.

Fig. 3. Aluminium melting furnace.

9

When melting brass or similar alloys, units rated at 60 kW can produce up to $5\frac{1}{2}$ tons in 24 hours. Daily outputs of 40 tons can be obtained from large units rated at 480 kW. Power consumption is approximately 220 kWh per ton. When melting nickel-silver or zinc the power consumption is 300 kWh and 120 kWh per ton respectively.

The smaller sizes always have a single transformer unit requiring a single-phase supply. Where it is necessary to employ a three-phase supply on a single unit furnace then a 3-phase to 1-phase static convertor can be used to give a reasonably well balanced load on the three-phase supply. The larger sizes are equipped with two transformer units which can be worked off a two-phase

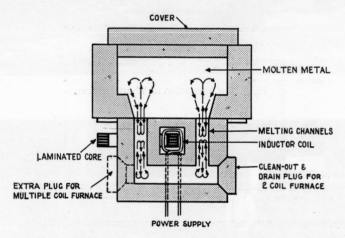

Fig. 4. Tama core-type induction furnace.

supply or with a 3/2-phase transformer from a three-phase system. The largest sizes are fitted with three transformer units for direct three-phase operation.

Figure 2 shows in operation part of an installation of twelve furnaces for melting brass. Each furnace is rated at 120 kW, the capacity of the bath being 1,200 lb. The axis of tilt of each furnace is at the pouring spout, so that a constant head of metal is maintained while pouring into the ingot moulds. These are mounted on turntables in front of the furnace. Each furnace unit is provided with a fume exhaust hood to keep the atmosphere of the shop clear of zinc fumes.

Induction melting of aluminium and its alloys enables increased purity to be obtained, there being a decrease of gas absorption, absence of segregation and elimination of oxide inclusions. Melting losses are low and with average alloys the metal loss is of the order of 0.8 per cent to 1 per cent when charging foundry ingots and only $1\frac{1}{2}$ per cent to 2 per cent when charging baled sheet or foil scrap. The power consumption for melting and superheating slightly is about 450 kWh per ton. When superheating is followed by a period of holding at temperature a power consumption between 525 kWh and 575 kWh per ton may be expected.

Furnaces of the original Ajax Wyatt type (Figure 1) are unsuitable for melting aluminium because an unavoidable accumulation

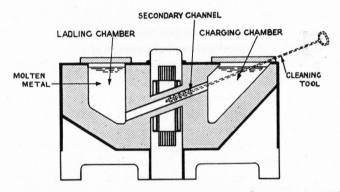

Fig. 5. Double chamber core-type induction furnace.

of oxide is deposited in the secondary channel. Reduction in the effective cross section of the channel slows up the rate of melting and when the channel becomes blocked, the current is interrupted.

Normal frequency furnaces have, therefore, been developed in which the secondary channel can be cleaned easily, and two well known types are illustrated in Figures 4 and 5.

The channel should be scraped and cleaned preferably twice every eight hours for most alloys and at least three times when melting silicon-containing alloys. Cleaning rods or specially designed hand tools may be used for the purpose.

The furnaces can be started easily from cold should the metal in the channel freeze up from power failure or other cause. Under normal working conditions it is preferable to keep the metal molten even when on stand-by. However, during a long period of shut down, the bath may be emptied and the metal drained from the channel. To start up again it will, of course, be necessary to re-charge the channel with molten metal.

The single chamber type of furnace (Figure 4) is very suitable for ingot work and an installation for melting aluminium for casting into rolling mill ingots is shown in Figure 3. The bath has a holding cap-acity of 10,000 lb. and a melting rate of 1¼ tons per hour. It is rated at 500 kW.

1.3 3 ALUMINIUM DIE-CASTING

When aluminium is to be alloyed with a constituent such as silicon for the production of die castings, it is usual to employ a large fur-nace for the primary melting of scrap. The molten metal is trans-ferred to a smaller furnace in which the alloying constituent is charged. The stirring forces which occur within the bath ensure mixing and a homogeneous composition of the alloy is obtained.

A furnace for the production of aluminium silicon alloy is shown in Figure 6. It has a holding capacity of 800 lb. and is supplying metal to two die-casting machines.

Frequently small holding furnaces are used to ensure a state of quiescence before casting. The metal level is maintained by trans-ferring molten metal from the alloying furnace.

The two-chamber furnace (Figure 5) is, therefore, of particular value to the die-casting industry, because it eliminates the necessity of having two furnaces and transferring metal from melting unit to holding unit.

Two chambers are provided instead of the usual single chamber. One chamber (the charging chamber), is for receiving ingots or molten metal. This chamber is connected to the second chamber (the ladling or pouring chamber) by melting channels. This second chamber, therefore, contains only molten metal—and ladling or pouring can take place continuously even though cold metal has just been added to the charging chamber.

The combined capacity of the two chambers is about 3 to 3½ times the required hourly output.

1.4 CORELESS INDUCTION HEATING

The submerged resistor or core type furnace, whilst extremely use-ful for melting aluminium, brass, nickel-silver, zinc, and other low melting point metals, has the disadvantage that the alloy melted in it cannot readily be changed, because a quantity of molten metal

Fig. 6. View of aluminium die-casting installation.

must always be retained to fill the heating channel and to cover the bottom of the bath.

Some metals have a vigorous reaction with the refractory lining, and since the materials which can be used for building the involved shape of the lining are limited in number, the range of metals and alloys which can be melted economically is therefore restricted.

The coreless induction furnace overcomes many of these restrictions. This type of furnace (Figure 7) is characterised by the inductor being a water cooled helical coil. The charge to be melted is held in a crucible of simple shape located inside the coil. The crucible may be of any non-conducting refractory material, or a high melting point metal, but the most economical crucible is that which is formed *in situ* from granulated refractory materials fritted together by the first charge melted in it.

A metal former or container having the inside dimensions of the crucible is located centrally in the inductor. The intervening space is rammed with the refractory mixture and the container packed with scrap metal. When power is applied to the inductor, the container melts, the heat glazing or fritting the inner face of the

13

refractory. Refractory linings prepared in this fashion are ideally suited to the unique thermal conditions of induction heating.

The lining may be acid, basic or neutral depending upon the metal to be melted. Acid linings are usual for high-speed tool steels, plain carbon steels and low-alloyed steels, special cast irons and for non-ferrous metals. Basic linings are suitable for stainless steel, high manganese steels and any steels where special slag reaction processes are carried out. Basic material is preferred for nickel-iron alloys.

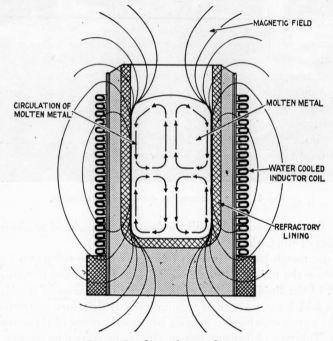

Fig. 7. Coreless induction furnace.

Coreless induction melting considerably widens the range of metals which can be dealt with on a practical scale and makes for greater flexibility since the crucible can be emptied completely at the end of the melt and the next charge may be of a different alloy provided it is of the same group.

To heat and melt the charge in the crucible the inductor is connected to an alternating current supply of a suitable frequency. Low frequency (normal mains frequency), high frequency, or radio frequency may be used. Each frequency band has its inherent uses and range of applications.

Owing to certain inherent electrical phenomena small pieces of metal cannot be heated to melting point by low frequency induction. Consequently this type of furnace is most suited to medium and large sizes which melt relatively large scrap. Large furnaces, having very high currents in the inductor coil cause most vigorous stirring forces in the molten metal. The rapid movement of metal whilst bringing about intimate mixing or alloying of the molten constituents, has the disadvantage of causing a high rate of wear on the refractory lining. Low frequency melting is unsuitable for the production of high grade steel since vigorous stirring makes it difficult to keep the bath covered with molten slag. Where metallurgical reactions are of less importance, however, and high rates of melting are not required, low frequency melting has the merit of low initial cost compared with that of the high frequency method of melting.

The normal frequency coreless induction furnace can be connected directly to a commercial 3-phase supply. The equipment additional to the furnace is essentially simple there being only a bank of capacitors together with their switches and also a main switch. Although the capacitors may be more costly than those on an H.F. installation of equivalent melting capacity, on balance the omission of a motor alternator set may reduce considerably the capital outlay required for a given output.

Although normal frequency installations are used for melting, holding or superheating molten metal from a cupola is likely to prove a more important application. A typical furnace rated at 120 kW having a holding capacity of 2,240 lb. will give a throughput of 5,000 lb. per hour of hot cupola metal superheated from 1,350°C to 1,450°C.

1.4 2 HIGH FREQUENCY MELTING FURNACE

The high frequency melting furnace is substantially similar to the low frequency furnace. The main difference is that a suitable source of high frequency supply must be available. Mains frequency can be converted to those frequencies representative of today's practice— from approximately 1,000 c.p.s. up to 5,000 c.p.s.—by
   a. Rotating equipment
   b. Static frequency changing equipment
   c. Spark-gap generator
   d. Electronic valve generator.

Fig. 8. A 3-ton high frequency induction furnace in a large steel works.

The more usual method for production melting is by means of rotating equipment. Essentially this comprises a motor generator driven by a normal electric motor and a bank of capacitors with an arrangement of switchgear to vary the number of capacitors in circuit to maintain a high power factor under the varying electrical conditions of the melt.

Static frequency changing equipment consists of a transformer, a mercury arc inverter and a bank of capacitors. A nominal frequency of about 2,000 c.p.s. may be considered the highest working frequency at present, although improved design technique may extend this to higher frequencies in the future.

1.4 3 STEEL

In making high-quality steels the high frequency melting furnace is an indispensable unit in any steel works whether it be large or small (Figures 8 and 9). The capital cost is higher than that of any other type of furnace but for certain metallurgical operations the overall running cost is less than that of other types. It is also cleaner and melts much more quickly. It is most efficient as a remelting unit

Fig. 9. Five-hundredweight high frequency induction furnace
in a small foundry.

where good quality raw materials are alloyed to make the highest
quality alloy steels, including stainless steel and high speed steel.
It is, however, not suitable for melting and refining low grade
assorted scrap. This work is best carried out in an electric arc
furnace.

To obtain maximum productivity and low operating costs, sufficient power should be available to complete the melting cycle
quickly. In ingot making the cycle should be completed in about
$1\frac{1}{2}$ hours for a furnace of 5 cwt capacity and $2\frac{1}{2}$ hours for a furnace
of about 5 tons capacity.

It is usual to install about 100 kW of generator capacity for each
ton of steel required per 8 hour shift. For small foundry work
where a higher temperature is required and a longer time is needed
for shanking, the allowance should be increased to 120 kW per ton.

B   17

Rotating equipment capable of developing from 10 kW up to 2,500 kW of generator output is in general use and furnace bodies are made in sizes varying from 28 lb up to 8 tons: the schedule of output data given below is representative of present day practice.

TABLE 1. Output data – induction melting

Generator output	Furnace size	Melting time	Output per 8 hour shift Ingot making	Foundry
50 kW	1 cwt	40 mins	10 cwt	7 cwt
	3 cwt	110 mins		
100 kW	1 cwt	20 mins	1 ton	15 cwt
	3 cwt	55 mins		
	5 cwt	90 mins		
150 kW	5 cwt	60 mins	$1\frac{1}{2}$ tons	1 ton
	10 cwt	110 mins		
300 kW	10 cwt	60 mins	3 tons	2 tons
	1 ton	105 mins		
650 kW	1 ton	60 mins	7 tons	7 tons*
	2 tons	100 mins		
1,500 kW	4 tons	100 mins	$17\frac{1}{2}$ tons	$17\frac{1}{2}$ tons*
	5 tons	115 mins		
1,800 kW	5 tons	95 mins	20 tons	20 tons*
	8 tons	150 mins		

* These figures are based on ladle pouring.

1.4 4 CHOICE OF FREQUENCY

For general work the following frequencies are representative:

Power	Frequency
Under 50 kW	5,000 cycles and over
50–200 kW	2,000 cycles
200–500 kW	1,500 cycles
500–1,200 kW	1,000 cycles
Over 1,200 kW	Less than 1,000 cycles

1.4 5 POWER CONSUMPTION

High speed steel can be melted for a power consumption of approximately 550/600 kWh per ton: low alloy steel and stainless steel require about 600/650 kWh and 650/700 kWh per ton respectively. Power consumption varies according to the size of the installation and the rate of melting but these figures may be taken for general guidance.

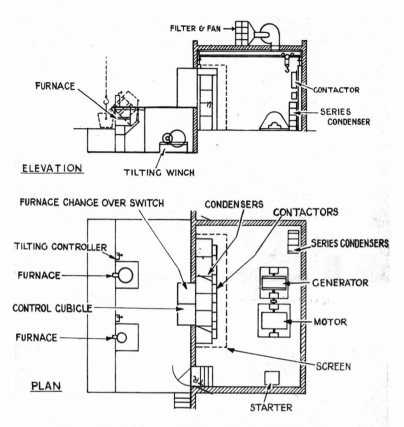

Fig. 10. Typical layout of H.F. coreless induction furnace.

1.46 LAYOUT OF PLANT

The diagram shown in Figure 10 is typical of a high frequency melting installation.

The motor generator is usually housed in a well ventilated substation which may be adjacent to the melting shop, or situated some distance away and operated by remote control. The capacitor bank should be within reasonable distance of the furnace in order to reduce the losses in the cables and busbars.

A well laid out high frequency motor generator substation is illustrated in Figure 11. Each generator unit comprises an 1,850 h.p. motor coupled to a 625 kW generator. The frequency is 1,125 cycles per second and the voltage 1,500.

It is customary to use furnaces of the nose trunnion tilting type,

Fig. 11. High frequency motor generator substation showing
two 625 kW sets.

Fig. 12. Steel-melting installation with four 15 cwt. induction furnaces.

the axis of the trunnion being at the axis of the spout for lip casting. The top of the furnace is usually flush with the charging and working platform which may be raised above the casting floor for easy slagging and cleaning. The essential features of a layout of this description are shown in Figure 12.

1.5 PRODUCTION MELTING — OTHER APPLICATIONS
1.5 1 CAST IRON

High frequency furnaces may be used for melting high grade cast iron and are particularly suitable for borings which can be melted far more quickly than in any externally heated crucible furnace. Even low grade cast iron is sometimes produced in this type of furnace using steel borings, cast iron borings and other scrap together with some pig iron. In localities where pig iron and coke is dear and electricity is cheap, then H.F. melting can cost less than cupola-melting.

Fig. 13. Spark-gap H.F. generator with 3 lb. melting furnace.

Fig. 14. 30 kW valve generator with 30 lb. melting furnace.

1.5 2 NON-FERROUS METALS

High melting point metals such as nickel and its alloys may be melted with advantage in the high frequency type of furnace. Much of the information given for steel applies equally to the melting of nickel.

When melting alloys, the composition of which may be changed over a sequence of heats, the coreless type of furnace should be used. When pouring, the crucible can be emptied completely, and then recharged for a subsequent heat with another alloy, preferably of the same class or group. A lift-off type of furnace can be of exceptional value to the jobbing foundry. Crucibles are used, but are not fixed in the furnace, the inductor being lowered over the crucible. When ready for pouring the furnace is raised and the crucible carried off with tongs for pouring. The furnace can then be immediately lowered over another crucible already charged.

The coreless furnace has also proved of particular advantage for melting magnesium. It shows considerable reduction in the metal loss by oxidation and a large reduction in the quantity of flux required. Steel crucibles backed by insulation are used; these have a very long life by comparison with normal fuel-fired furnaces.

1.6 DUAL FREQUENCY FURNACES

In the H.F. coreless induction furnace stirring of the charge always takes place during melting. The degree of stirring can be controlled to some extent in the design of the equipment. It is dependent upon the frequency chosen for the particular metal and size of furnace. In cases where volatile additions are required to be made to the charge it is possible to arrange for the electro-magnetic stirring of the charge to continue without increasing its temperature; this is accomplished by the application of a low frequency supply to the furnace coil when the H.F. power is switched off, the arrangement then being known as a dual frequency furnace. In this way the metals which form the base of the alloy can be fully melted, the additions put into the charge, and the whole can then be stirred without superheating the base metals. There is, therefore, a minimum loss of volatiles. At the same time adequate mixing can be ensured and completed more quickly than by any other method.

1.7 SMALL SCALE MELTING

Induction furnaces of much smaller capacity than those employed for normal production melting may be used for research work in the laboratory for the melting of precious metals such as gold, silver and platinum. Where heats of small quantities of metals or alloys are required there is no better method than heating by induction.

The most convenient sources of power for these small furnaces are the spark-gap generator and the valve generator.

The spark-gap generator is a single phase unit and high frequency

Fig. 15. Casting copper ingots from a 35 lb. radio frequency induction furnace.

Fig. 16. Induction melting furnace and accessories in vacuum tank.

current is generated by the discharge of a bank of capacitors through a mercury spark gap. It is suitable for frequencies from about 20,000 c.p.s. up to 50,000 c.p.s.

The valve generator, of which more details are given in Chapter 2 is an attractive alternative. Oscillator valves are becoming more efficient, and radio frequency melting may well extend into the field in which spark-gap and small motor generators are now used.

The application of a spark-gap equipment is shown in Figure 13. A generator, having an output of 6 kW can melt 3 lb. of steel in 30 minutes, whilst 200 oz. of gold can be melted in approximately 8 minutes with a 20 kW unit.

A 30 kW valve generator is shown in Figure 14 for melting 30 lb. of steel in about 20 to 25 minutes. A 35 lb. charge of molten copper being poured is shown in Figure 15.

1.8 VACUUM MELTING

Since heat is generated in the work itself, the melting may be carried out in a protective atmosphere at any pressure, or in a vacuum.

Consistently pure metal for certain duties may be obtained by melting, pouring and casting in vacuo. This ensures freedom from gaseous contamination, and any diffused or entrapped gases which may be emitted as the metal becomes hot are drawn off by the vacuum pump.

The complete furnace and the mould is placed within a steel shell which is connected to a vacuum pumping equipment and mechanical means are provided so that the pouring and casting operations may be carried out without breaking the vacuum. One arrangement is to pour the metal into the mould by tilting the furnace within the vacuum chamber. Another arrangement is to have the furnace integral with the vessel and to tilt the whole vessel, the mould being mounted on trunnions inside it. A still further arrangement is for the furnace, mould and vessel to be moved together.

The first arrangement is illustrated in Figure 16. The vacuum chamber is shown with the cover removed and clearly depicts the assembly of the furnace and the mould. The high frequency furnace coil is of normal construction but all coil supports are vacuum impregnated to obviate the need for outgassing after each exposure of the furnace to atmosphere. The refractory lining is of normal construction.

Two chargers are provided, the main one holds up to one third

Fig. 17. Vacuum equipment for melting furnace.

of the total charge which can be added during the melt and the other is sub-divided into six compartments from which alloy additions may be made in any desired sequence during the course of the melt.

The general layout of the installation (Figure 17) shows the vacuum tank, the pumping equipment and the associated control valves and pipework.

The tank illustrated can accommodate a furnace of 56 lb. melting capacity.

Vacuum melting furnaces, used for research work and small scale production, range in size from about 10 lb. up to $\frac{1}{2}$ cwt, but in the future in industries where purer metals than those hitherto obtainable are required, larger units are practicable and will be widely used. Furnaces of one ton capacity have already been put into service for production melting.

1.9 INVESTMENT PRECISION CASTING

The 'investment' or 'lost wax' process of casting consists in forming a heat-resisting or refractory mould around a pattern of a low melting point. When the mould has hardened, the pattern is melted away, leaving an accurate cavity to receive the metal. The advantages of the process are numerous. Metals which are too hard for machining may be cast to close tolerances; castings which require little or no machining can replace expensive fabricated assemblies; and a high degree of surface finish can be produced.

But success is obtainable only by close control of metallurgical reactions. The temperature of the melt, and the time taken to fill the mould are important.

Induction melting is one practical solution and has been widely used. High melting point alloys can be made with repetitive consistency, melted rapidly and poured under controlled conditions of temperature.

PART TWO

2

Induction heating
for metallurgical purposes

2.1 GENERAL

Induction heating is not just another method of heating, but it is a method by which accurately controlled amounts of heat can be generated in an object and concentrated just where it can be employed most effectively. Further the process can be repeated precisely in successive applications.

When a conductor carrying an alternating current is designed intentionally for the purpose of inducing eddy currents in the surface of an object it is called an inductor or work coil.

The shape of this coil, the magnitude of the current flowing through it, and the position relative to the object to be heated determines the 'where' and 'how' of the heating effect. The duration of the heating cycle determines the 'quantity' of heat generated in the object.

There is no basic difference between heating at a frequency of 50 cycles per second or at 500,000 cycles per second, except that certain effects become more pronounced the higher the frequency.

2.2 SURFACE HEATING

In the introduction it has been noted that alternating currents are most dense on the surface of the conductor. This is called 'skin effect'. The current induced in the work is similarly distributed. The higher the frequency the more pronounced this effect becomes.

A layer called the 'depth of current penetration' may be determined by the formula:

$$\text{Depth in cms.} = 5 \times \sqrt{\frac{\text{P (resistivity in michroms)}}{\text{U (permeability) x f (frequency)}}}$$

For a given material the depth of penetration is, therefore, inversely proportional to the frequency. The effective depth of heat penetration, however, is always greater than the depth of current penetration because heating takes a finite time so that thermal conduction towards the centre takes place during that time.

To obtain a shallow case the heating time must be short which entails a high concentration of power as well as high frequency. Because of this, there is a minimum depth of effective heating which it is possible to accomplish at any frequency.

2.2 1 SELECTION OF FREQUENCY

In the choice of the most suitable frequency, the size of the component and the metallurgical requirements are determining factors. Table 2 shows the effect of size on frequency. The figures relate to steel when heated above its magnetic change point.

TABLE 2. Heating steel by induction

Frequency cycles per second	Minimum depth of hardness inches	Minimum diameter which may be surface hardened efficiently inches	Minimum diameter for efficient through heating inches
50	—	—	6.00
3,000	0.060	1.25	0.75
10,000	0.040	0.75	0.40
500,000	0.020	0.25	0.13

It will be clear from these figures that the higher the frequency the larger the range of parts which can be heated efficiently when surface hardening is required.

The size of the generating plant and, therefore, its initial cost is determined by the size of the largest object which is required to be surface heated.

The size of the smallest object may determine the most suitable frequency but considerable latitude is permissible—the primary consideration is capital outlay.

2.2 2 HEATING TIMES

The rate at which the surface of an object may be heated depends upon the power concentration. By heating quickly the effect can be confined to a thin surface layer. With slower heating, thermal conduction carries the heat into the body of the metal (Figure 18), without the surface being seriously overheated.

An approximate guide for surface hardening is to apply energy to the heated area at a rate of 35 kW-secs. per sq. in. Power densities varying from 5 kW up to 50 kW per sq. in. may be chosen. The transfer of equivalent amounts of energy are then obtained by applying 5 kW per sq. in. for 7 seconds, 35 kW for one second, or 50 kW for 0.7 seconds. Metallurgical requirements determine the rate of heating and consequently the size of the plant. The rapid heating

| 3 SECONDS | 12 SECONDS | 27 SECONDS | 48 SECONDS |

Fig. 18. H.F. induction heating is most dense on the surface of the metal. The diagram shows the heat penetration, by conduction from the surface, as the heating time is increased.

which is characteristic of induction heating minimises oxidation and reduces distortion. It is, therefore, preferable to select the highest rate of heating which the conditions will permit.

2.3 SOURCES OF ELECTRICAL ENERGY

Four sources of energy for induction heating are in general use today. Figures 19–22 show in schematic form typical arrangements.

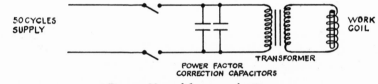

50 CYCLES SUPPLY

WORK COIL

POWER FACTOR CORRECTION CAPACITORS

TRANSFORMER

Fig. 19. Normal frequency heating.

1. NORMAL FREQUENCY SUPPLY (Figure 19). For this no local generating plant is required. This represents a big saving in first cost; for this reason normal frequency is sometimes used in applications where high frequency would be more efficient.

2. ROTATING EQUIPMENT (Figure 20) consists of a high frequency generator driven by a normal electric motor. This type of equipment is usual for frequencies from 2,000 to 10,000 cycles per second. Sizes commonly used range from 50 kW up to 150 kW, but most individual applications are between 100 kW and 150 kW.

3. STATIC FREQUENCY CHANGING EQUIPMENT (Figure 21) consists of a controlled mercury arc, for frequencies up to 3,000 cycles per second. For the moment a frequency of about 2,000 cycles per second is most commonly used.

4. ELECTRONIC EQUIPMENT (Figure 22) consists of a valve generator, for higher frequencies. A frequency of around 400,000

C

cycles per second is in common use. Today's practical applications of R.F. heating involve generators having R.F. outputs ranging from 1 kW to 50 kW.

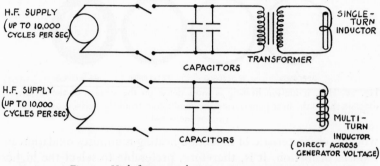

Fig. 20. High frequency heating – motor generator.

Each source of supply has its own general field of application. The electronic valve generator, with its higher frequency is most suitable for small parts and, therefore, moderately low powers are most commonly required. It is versatile in so far as for most work the

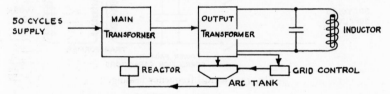

Fig. 21. High frequency heating – static converter.

inductors are simple. They can easily be made to follow the contour of the work and they may be constructed or adjusted readily on site. The scope of induction heating has widened very considerably since the radio frequency generator became available for industrial purposes. Although there may be some overlapping of radio frequency and high frequency, the choice will then be decided by the particular circumstances.

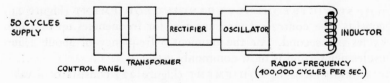

Fig. 22. Radio frequency heating.

34

2.4 SITE LOCATION AND MAINTENANCE OF GENERATORS

1. ROTATING EQUIPMENT. High frequency generators of the rotary type are mostly air cooled and are usually installed in a sub-station ventilated with filtered air. The generator set can, however, have a water cooled heat exchanger built together with it, which enables the set to be placed in the production line near the heater station.

A typical high frequency motor generator substation is shown in Figure 23. There are two 150 kW 10,000 cycle 500 volt generators driven from a common motor of 550 h.p. High frequency power is transmitted to the work stations by co-axial cables laid in under-ground trenches.

Fig. 23. Substation for induction heating comprising four 150 kW generators.

A totally enclosed generator and heat exchanger set is shown in Figure 24. The equipment is installed in the heart of a motor-car assembly shop.

More recently, totally enclosed vertical spindle water cooled motor generators, as shown in Figure 25, have been developed. The units illustrated each have an output of 210 kW at a frequency of 8,300 cycles per second. Temperature of the water in the cooling jacket is controlled, and should there be an interruption in the water service for any reason the machine is closed down automatically. The noise level is low, being at least one third that of the normal air cooled unit. The generator has no objectionable noise features and it may, therefore, be installed right in the production line. Specially prepared

Fig. 24. Two totally enclosed H.F. motor generators each 150 kW.

Fig. 25. Vertical spindle water-cooled H.F. generators.

foundations are unnecessary, and the H.F. installation may therefore be sited in the position best suited to the mechanical handling features of the factory.

Generator sets require no more than routine attention and maintenance which is normally given to all electric power equipment.

2. ELECTRONIC VALVE EQUIPMENT. The valve generator unit has essentially 50 cycle switchgear and control section, a rectifier section and oscillator section.

The three sections—control, rectifier, and oscillator—may be built separately, or alternatively combined in one enclosure. If built separately, the oscillator may be installed some distance away from the other units. A typical self-contained unit is shown in Figure 26.

Fig. 26. Typical R.F. generator 50 kW for induction hardening.

Since the control and rectifier sections comprise ordinary electrical components no specialist knowledge is required for their maintenance.

The oscillator section is, however, of a specialist nature and not every works electrician is yet trained in the technique of electronic engineering. Surface dirt and contamination can cause serious surface leakage of electricity at radio frequencies. These leakages may impair the efficiency of the plant and it may be advisable, therefore, for the makers to carry out a routine inspection several times a year to check over and clean.

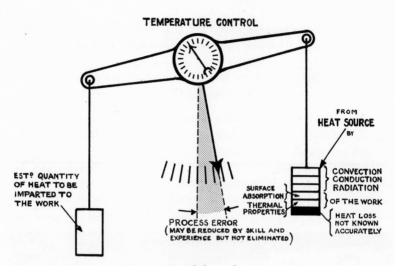

Fig. 27. Heat balance diagram.

The equipment is usually mounted in a dust-proof enclosure with which is incorporated some form of cooling, primarily for the valves; this may be by air or water. Where air cooling is used, filters are provided. The only maintenance is the regular cleaning of these. Unless softened water is used, frequent and regular cleaning of the water system is necessary.

2.5 INTERFERENCE WITH SOUND BROADCAST AND OTHER RADIO SERVICES

The frequency selected for R.F. induction heating lies between the medium and long wave broadcast bands. It is customary, therefore, to provide filters in the supply leads to the equipment to suppress the leakage of the R.F. power to the mains system, and in normal circumstances no interference will be caused to radio reception. Where there is a risk of radiation from a large R.F. installation, the entire equipment can be housed in a simple enclosure of expanded metal, or galvanised iron wire gauze, and, to be effective, as well as for reasons of safety, the screening should be efficiently earthed. (See G.P.O. Publication C.2201 *Methods of Screening Industrial, Scientific and Medical Radio Frequency Equipment.*)

2.6 CONTROL OF INDUCTION HEATING OPERATIONS

Induction heating is the only heating process, with the exception of direct resistance heating, which develops heat in the part itself.

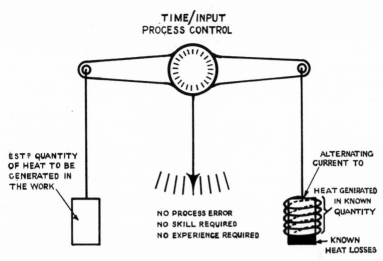

Fig. 28. Heat balance diagram.

The amount of heat thus generated is dependent only upon the heating time and the power input.

When, therefore, the heating operation is carried out by controlling the time and power input, the heating cycle may be repeated an indefinite number of times with absolute consistency and dependable results.

The analogy of a simple balance shown in Figures 27 and 28 illustrates the difference between heating from an external source and induction heating.

When heating from an external source the heat is transferred to the work by conduction, convection and radiation, but it is only the temperature of the surroundings which is controlled. The amount of heat which flows into the work is dependent upon its surface conditions which may fluctuate and, therefore, the amount of heat which is absorbed in a fixed time is variable.

When heat is generated in the work by induction methods it is the total amount of energy which is controlled. The same amount of energy always produces the same results and a high degree of accuracy may be obtained with extremely high rates of production.

2.7 GENERAL PRODUCTION ADVANTAGES ENSUING FROM THE USE OF INDUCTION HEATING

The use of induction heating in a well chosen application produces a better quality, in less time and at a lower cost. Contributory factors are rapid heating, precision of heating, and increased production without using skilled labour.

The rate of heating—the most rapid so far known—results in far less scaling than occurs with other methods of heating without the need for a protective atmosphere; hence the usual subsidiary operations and related handling are done away with.

In hardening, the symmetry of heating and consequently of quenching, and the fact that only the zone requiring hardening is heated, results in much less distortion than by other heating methods. Subsequent operations such as straightening or grinding may be reduced and frequently eliminated. Waste of heat is avoided because only the selected parts are heated. No separate treatment is required to be given to those surfaces which are not to be hardened. Precise control of heating permits uniform metallurgical reactions to occur and for the results to be repeated accurately.

The cleanliness, coolness and compactness of this method of heating enables it to be used directly in the production line, many handling operations are eliminated and greater productivity is obtained from a reduced floor space.

It can be said that induction heating gives a machine-tool quality of precision to heating which no other method does. It allows excellent working conditions and has the highest possible production rate. It thus makes possible automatic working in a production line.

3

Normal mains frequency heating

3.1 TYPICAL USES

Preheating and stress relieving fabricated parts.
Heating large components in stainless steel and in titanium.
Preheating of steel tubes for manipulation and forming.
Heating for shrinking.
Heating billets for forging and extrusion.
Heating steel autoclaves for chemical processing.
Press platen heating.

Normal mains frequency induction heating does not differ basically from other forms of induction heating but the energy for it may be taken from the electricity power supply system. No local generator is necessary and this represents a large saving in the first cost of the equipment.

It has limits of practical application, depending upon the size of the work and other factors, but the consideration of first cost may be so important that normal frequency is sometimes used where similar but more efficient results could be obtained were high frequency heating to be employed.

3.2 PREHEATING AND STRESS RELIEVING OF WELDED JOINTS

It is necessary to use high quality heat resisting steels for the manufacture of pipework for the distribution systems of high pressure steam in modern power stations, and to employ similar materials in the construction of chemical plant such as autoclaves and for the fabrication of distillation columns and cracking vessels.

The parts are fabricated by welding but these special steels cannot be welded satisfactorily when cold. The intense heat of welding is localised and highly concentrated so that internal stresses are set up. Owing to the lack of ductility in the cold metal these stresses are likely to result in the weld being cracked, not only on the surface but also internally, and they also cause the work to distort. Pre-heating before welding prepares the metal to absorb these stresses and to equalise them thus enabling a uniform weld to be achieved free from flaws. The welding is carried out after the work has reached a satisfactory temperature. When the welding operation has been completed it is then necessary to give a final heat treatment at a somewhat higher temperature than for pre-heating and it is preferable for this treatment to follow immediately after the welding.

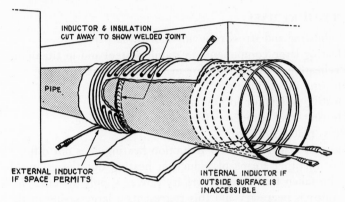

Fig. 29. Preheating and stress relieving of welded pipes *in situ*. Induction heating can be applied from the inside if the outside surfaces are inaccessible.

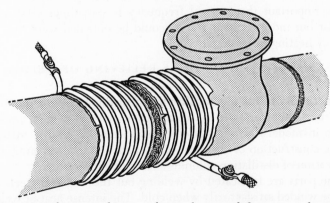

Fig. 30. Preheating and stress relieving by normal frequency induction.

Cooling must be avoided between the two treatments otherwise the quality of the joint may be impaired.

Customary methods of heating are very limited in their application and may become impracticable when dealing with components which are bulky, have thick walls, or where the joints are in inaccessible positions.

Heating by induction is the answer to many of the difficult problems involved. The treatment may be carried out in confined spaces where combustion heating methods would be impossible, and should the welded joint be inaccessible from the outside, then induction heating may be applied from the inside—see Figure 29.

Bulky or intricate constructions may be welded on site thus avoiding high transport costs. Erection work may be simplified and the completion of some important industrial installation may be accelerated.

A length of copper alloy cable is wrapped round the part to be heated. The cable is specially insulated to withstand the temperatures involved (about 450°C for pre-heating and 650°C for annealing). The number of turns used depends upon the application (Figure 30).

When an alternating current of electricity is passed through the cable, heat is generated in the work which acts as the short circuited secondary of a transformer, the cable being the primary winding. The use of power from the mains has the advantage of extreme simplicity and low first cost as it only requires a low voltage transformer with simple switchgear. On the other hand a relatively large number of turns is required if a satisfactory high power input is to be obtained, and in some applications the current becomes so high that an unwieldy size of cable would be required. It would then be preferable to use high frequency heating—see Paragraph 8.4, Chapter 8.

3.3 STRESS RELIEVING IN WELDED FABRICATIONS, FORGINGS AND CASTINGS

Hot working of metals produces internal stresses and unless these are removed distortion or cracking of the component may occur. They can be removed by heat treatment, typical objects being large forgings, castings and welded structures.

If ordinary convection furnaces were used for a bulky structure, it would need a very large and expensive furnace, which would have high running costs.

Localised heating by induction is more practical and more flexible.

Induction heating minimises the formation of oxide and scale on machined parts. The method is thermally efficient because heat is produced only where it is required; there is no absorption of heat by furnace refractories, and no extraneous nor standby losses.

The heating cycle may be determined in advance and metallurgical reactions controlled within close limits simply by the variation of the current in the inductor. Heat is generated within the metal so that internal stresses and consequent deformation are reduced to a minimum.

Many applications may be carried out with a normal frequency supply but greater flexibility and better control is obtainable with high frequency.

3.4 HEATING FOR SHRINKING

The hot shrinking of tyres on to wheel blanks of large gear wheels and turbine discs on to shafts and of starter rings on flywheels may be carried out accurately, rapidly, and efficiently, both at normal frequency and at higher frequencies.

The parts can be heated uniformly so that distortion can be avoided, while perfect tightening is ensured when they are cooled.

When dealing with large bulky parts the heating inductor may comprise a coil of insulated flexible cable placed against the faces of the heated parts, but when quantity production is involved work stations with suitably designed fixtures are, of course, required.

Figures 31 and 32 illustrate typical yoke type normal frequency work stations for hot shrinking. The iron core is shown clearly in Figure 32. A section of the core is hinged for inserting it into the work. The automobile starter ring gears approximately 12 in. diameter, shown in Figure 32, are heated in approximately 20 seconds each and transferred by hand to an adjacent press for fitting to the flywheels.

3.5 BILLET HEATING

The heating of non-ferrous billets for extrusion requires large furnaces situated adjacent to the press.

Metals such as aluminium, aluminium alloys, copper and brass are all good conductors of heat, but the surfaces of these metals possess low heat absorption qualities. Rates of heating are slow and long soaking periods are required to ensure uniformity of temperature through the billet. There must be no hold-up of the costly extrusion press and the temperature of the furnace must, therefore, be maintained also during shut down periods if there is to be no delay in starting up.

When induction heating is employed significant savings of capital and running costs are shown. Less floor space is required because heating is rapid. There is close control of temperature because the heat is generated within the material itself. No time is lost after a period of shut down because there is no furnace to heat up. The

Fig. 31. Iron core normal frequency station for hot shrinking.

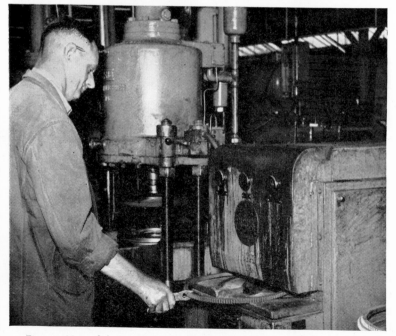

Fig. 32. Normal frequency heater for hot shrinking of small components.

Fig. 33. Aluminium billet heater, normal frequency. Output 1 ton per hour.

consumption of electricity is low, represented only by the heat absorbed by the charge, and that extracted by the cooling water which circulates through the inductor coils. Current is not consumed during non-working periods and there is no heating of unnecessary parts. Typical normal frequency induction heaters are illustrated. The unit shown in Figure 33 is rated at 300 kW nominal and has an output of one ton per hour of pure aluminium slabs heated to 500°C. A typical size of slab is 27 in. × 17 in. × 5 in. As each slab is pushed into the inductor a heated slab is discharged at the other end where it is carried by tongs to the rolling mill. Power is supplied from a transformer which has tappings for adjusting the power input. A bank of oil immersed capacitors is used to correct the power factor to 0.9. The complete installation measures 14 ft. × 9 ft., covering a floor area of 126 sq. ft.

The furnace of equal output which the induction heater replaced occupied a floor area of 410 sq. ft.

An inductor for heating aluminium alloy or magnesium billets is shown in Figure 34. It is rated at 250 kW with a mains loading of 300 kVA for an output of 1,700 lb. per hour. The billets are $8\frac{5}{8}$ in. diameter, varying from $7\frac{1}{2}$ in. to 36 in. in length. A hydraulic charging mechanism is used for random length operation. The photograph is taken from the discharge end of the inductor. The metal enclosure has been removed to show the construction of the water cooled coil.

Varying heating times are required for different metals or alloys. These are pre-set by means of a process timer so that the equipment may be operated by unskilled labour.

Furnaces heated by gas or electricity occupy three or four times the floor area of induction heaters and depending upon the method of firing and the type of conveyor mechanism used cost some 50 per cent. to 100 per cent. more than induction heating equipment of equivalent output. The larger the output the more economical does induction heating become. Comparative figures for heating $\frac{1}{2}$ ton of aluminium per hour, on the basis of single shift working, are given in the following table.

TABLE 3. Heating aluminium billets – comparative figures

	Gas at 450 BThUs per c.ft.	Electric resistance	Electric induction
Overall consumption per ton	3,500 c.ft.	335 kWh	280 kWh

Fig. 34. Inductor – normal frequency billet heater. Output 1,700 lbs. per hour of aluminium alloy.

47

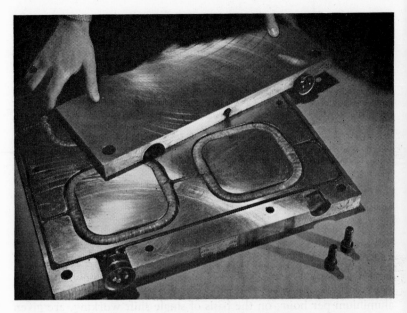

Fig. 35. Inductor coils for platen heating.

3.6 INDUCTION HEATING FOR THE WORKING OF PLASTICS

The development of the plastics industry has created new heating problems. Plastics of the thermo-setting group are formed to shape by press moulding, injection moulding or extruding.

Heat as well as pressure plays an important part in their processing. Press platens, injection chambers and extrusion cylinders must be heated to bring about the complete polymerisation or curing which is necessary for the production of the material.

The metal parts may be heated conductively by means of gas, steam or electric resistance elements, but greater heating efficiency and rapid generation of heat is secured by eddy current heating which can be controlled accurately.

When inductor coils are built into the body of the platen, as illustrated in Figure 35 and an alternating current at mains frequency is passed through them, heat is generated in the platen. Inductors may also be fitted easily to the appropriate parts of injection moulding machines and extrusion machines to heat the parts in a similar way. Surges of excessive temperature with the consequent waste of power are avoided. The temperature control responds quickly and heat losses are considerably reduced.

Fig. 36. Inductively heated platen on moulding press for plastics.

A typical moulding press in which induction heaters are built into the body of the lower platen is shown in Figure 36. The pellets are preheated in a dielectric heater before being placed into the mould cavity.

Moulding times and pressures are reduced. Tool wear is also cut down considerably.

An 8 oz. injection moulding machine fitted with induction heaters is shown in Figure 37. In addition to the three narrow and one wide unit visible there is a further exterior heater unit on the nozzle of

D

Fig. 37. Injection moulding machine with induction heaters.

the machine and a flat heater in the flange which connects the heating chamber to the feed cylinder. Heat is generated all through the walls of the injection chamber and in the spreader. The plastic is heated all round, instead of on one face only, so that polymerisation is more complete and even.

Induction heating can be used for heating the cylinders of extrusion machines. Where other heating methods such as gas, steam, or resistance heaters slow up production the application of induction heating can increase it by bringing about more rapid and uniform polymerisation to give a better product.

Induction heating makes for higher productivity because :

1. Heat is generated in the metal parts deeply and evenly without there being temperature gradients. There are negligible tem-

perature changes at the moulding surface. This results in better and more accurately controlled heating of the material and consequently more consistent polymerisation.

2. The heating units have a high thermal efficiency and heat can be concentrated where it is required. Consequently there is a wider choice of conditions for processing and demands that cannot be met by other methods can be catered for.

3. Conditions for moulding the material are improved, leading to the quick production of good quality products, with less current consumption and negligible maintenance costs.

4

Surface hardening
by H.F. induction heating

4.1 GENERAL

High frequency induction heating provides a versatile and efficient
production method for the repetition hardening of steel parts, resulting in a hard skin and a tough core. It is a method of treating
all steels which are capable of being hardened and provides a manufacturing technique applicable to most engineering components
such as:

Ball heads for motor car ball pins
Crankshafts
Camshafts and wheels
Calculating machine parts
Film sprocket teeth
Gears (single shot and progressive)
Governor and rocker pads
Gob tubes
Hacksaw blade edges
Internal splines
Internal hardening of bores and holes in
  discs
Lawn mower cutter blades and cylinders
Pliers and cutters
Parts for accounting machines
Rails

Shafts, splined ends
Stub axles
Starter rings
Starter and locking nuts
Screwed bar
Shackle pins
Scissor blades
Tractor track pins
Track rollers and links
Tractor shoes
Tank turret ring ball tracks
Typewriter keys
Taps and adjustable dies
Valve seatings
Valve stems
Windscreen wiper shafts

4.2 METALLURGICAL DESCRIPTION

A plain carbon steel consists of pure iron and carbon together with
a few impurities. The carbon is in the form of iron carbide and it
forms, with the pure iron, an intimate mixture called 'pearlite'.
There is a definite ratio between the quantities of pure iron ferrite
and iron carbide in this mixture. When the steel is heated to a certain temperature, the form of the iron changes from the normal,
or alpha state, to the high temperature, or gamma state which has
a different crystal structure. Iron carbide will dissolve in the latter
but not in the former. The carbide first starts to dissolve in that
part of the iron mixed with it as pearlite, then, as the temperature
rises, it diffuses into the remainder. If the steel is allowed to cool

slowly the reverse happens, but if it is cooled rapidly there is no time for the carbide to deposit from solution. The iron nevertheless changes back to its normal alpha crystal state, so that the carbide is trapped in solution in the alpha iron in which it is not normally soluble. By doing this it distorts the crystal structure and the steel thus treated becomes hard.

The degree of hardness which is obtainable depends upon the amount of carbon in the steel. The depth to which the steel can be hardened depends upon the rapidity with which it can be cooled at depth. The temperature must be reduced below a certain critical value in a very short time—perhaps one or two seconds. Water quenching is most frequently used, but some steels require quenching in oil. Rapid cooling is possible at and near the surface, but deeper down the cooling rate is slower, and there comes a point when hardening does not occur because the rate of cooling is so slow that carbide deposits from solution. The depth at which hardening ceases is known as the hardenability depth. This varies according to quenching conditions. Alloying elements have the property of combining either with the carbon to form carbides, or entering the iron, making the critical cooling rate much slower, hence permitting deeper hardening.

Many steel components used in the construction of modern machines require hard surfaces. Some of them are to resist wear, in which case only a thin skin of hardness is necessary. Others are to have great strength so that the hardness requires to be relatively deep but closely controlled.

The traditional method of surface hardening is to start by making the component from a low carbon steel, and then to raise the carbon content of the surface only. This may be done by placing it in intimate contact with a medium of a carbonaceous nature, and raising the whole to a high temperature in a furnace. If the component is required to be hardened to a greater depth than a few thousandths of an inch then a very long heating time is required to effect the penetration of the carbon. After it is removed from the furnace, the component with the carbonaceous material has to be cooled for unpacking. It then has to be heated again for quenching to develop hardness which occurs in layers which have absorbed carbon. *Two* heating processes are thus involved and serious distortion of the part may occur.

When induction heating methods are used the component should be made from a medium carbon steel which needs no further processing before hardening. There is one heating operation only; the rate of heating may be extremely high and may be controlled closely; the quench can be regulated positively so that uniform metallurgical results can be obtained with precision when using unskilled labour; distortion is minimised; heat is conserved because the high rate of heating enables the surface alone to be heated leaving the core unaffected. The hardening operation can be carried out by an induction machine placed in the production line. The method is clean, shop conditions are improved, and productivity may be greatly accelerated.

There are some special cases where the shape of the component is complicated or its section is very thin, so that it is difficult to concentrate the induced power which would be necessary for the surface hardening of a selected area. In such cases as these low carbon steel, which is surface carburised, must often be resorted to. The cost of manufacture can be greatly reduced by induction heating for the hardening operation. Local areas can be hardened without the need for selective carburising, thus avoiding the necessity for plating or other stopping off methods.

Cast iron can also be surface hardened by induction methods. Malleable cast irons when properly heat treated combine the strength of forgings with the adaptability of castings. They have good ductility, high shock resistance, and when a hard wear-resisting surface is developed by induction hardening, a component can be produced at a much lower cost than by conventional methods.

4.3 FACTORS INVOLVED

The component to be hardened is shown in Figure 38. The inductor which surrounds it is fed with current from a high frequency source. The frequency is not critical but it will be governed by the size of the component while the shape of the inductor will be determined by the zone which is required to be hardened.

Basic types of inductors are shown diagrammatically in Figures 39–42. All inductors are cooled by passing water through the bore and typical examples designed for high frequency operation are illustrated in Figure 43.

A shows a pancake type inductor for heating plane surfaces and B iron cored inductors for a similar purpose. Inductor C is a channel type for heating the ends of bolt blanks. D is a single-turn inductor, split type with self-contained quench for hardening the pin and main journals of crankshafts. E is a single-turn inductor and F a multi-turn.

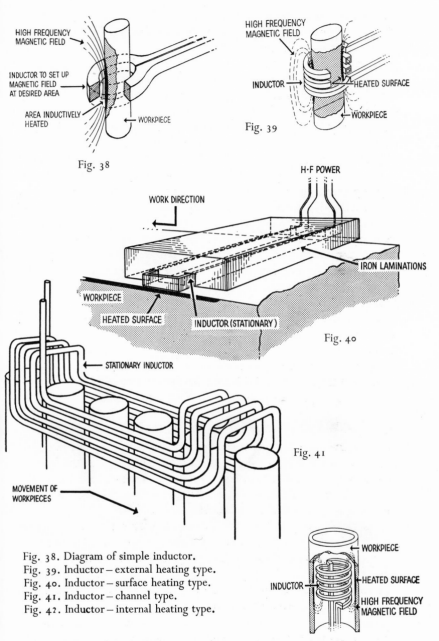

HIGH FREQUENCY MAGNETIC FIELD

INDUCTOR TO SET UP MAGNETIC FIELD AT DESIRED AREA

AREA INDUCTIVELY HEATED

WORKPIECE

Fig. 38

HIGH FREQUENCY MAGNETIC FIELD

INDUCTOR

HEATED SURFACE

WORKPIECE

Fig. 39

WORK DIRECTION

H·F POWER

IRON LAMINATIONS

WORKPIECE

HEATED SURFACE

INDUCTOR (STATIONARY)

Fig. 40

STATIONARY INDUCTOR

Fig. 41

MOVEMENT OF WORKPIECES

WORKPIECE

INDUCTOR

HEATED SURFACE

HIGH FREQUENCY MAGNETIC FIELD

Fig. 42

Fig. 38. Diagram of simple inductor.
Fig. 39. Inductor – external heating type.
Fig. 40. Inductor – surface heating type.
Fig. 41. Inductor – channel type.
Fig. 42. Inductor – internal heating type.

55

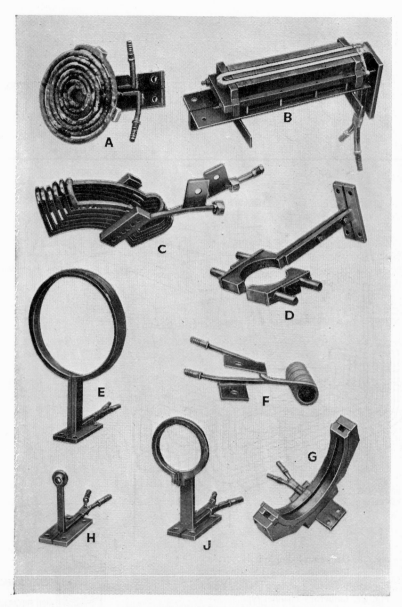

Fig. 43. Typical H.F. inductors.

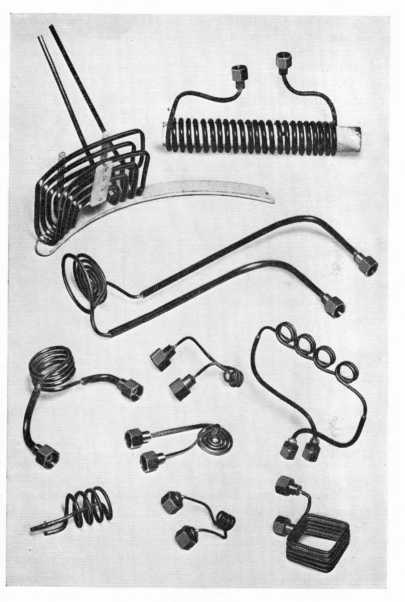

Fig. 44. Typical R.F. inductors.

G is an inductor without iron core, for heating the treads of track rollers, the flanges of which do not permit the component to be passed into a helical inductor. *H* is a single-turn inductor for the progressive hardening of track pins. *J* is another type of single-turn inductor.

Work coils designed specifically for hardening small parts by radio frequency heating are represented in Figure 44. The simple construction permits many of them to be made on site.

The effect of coupling, that is the gap between the surface of the work and the inductor is important. In general, the closer the coupling, the higher the efficiency of heating.

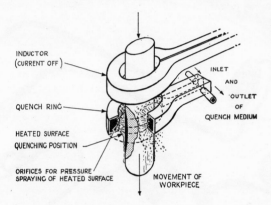

INDUCTOR
(CURRENT OFF)

INLET

AND

OUTLET

OF

QUENCH MEDIUM

QUENCH RING

HEATED SURFACE
QUENCHING POSITION

ORIFICES FOR PRESSURE
SPRAYING OF HEATED SURFACE

MOVEMENT OF
WORKPIECE

Fig. 45. Progressive heating and hardening – diagram of a simple inductor and separate quench ring.

The use of induction heating for producing a general and localised effect is almost unlimited. The products may range for example from components such as crankshafts for large engines, down to very small parts for calculating machines.

The following factors are involved in the treatment of any component:

1. Select the frequency. Reference has already been made to this in Paragraph 2.2.1.

2. Design the inductor – to produce the required zone of heating. Generally, each component requires its own inductor.

3. Design the quench. This may be in the form of a perforated ring, a series of jets or other arrangement, the purpose of which is to cool the heated parts as required.

4. Select the handling. Manual operation or completely mechanised handling equipment can be chosen.

5. Determine the method of heating. A choice can be made between progressive heating (Figure 45), or single shot methods (Figure 46). With progressive or continuous treatment one part follows another for as long as parts are fed to the machine. The power and speed are held constant all the time.

In the single shot method there is no linear movement between the inductor and the work. The work may be quenched immediately

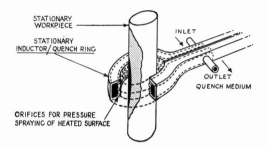

Fig. 46. Stationary heating and hardening – diagram of a combined inductor and quench ring for single shot working.

after heating, whilst still in the inductor, but for the most advantageous use of power one component can be heated whilst another is being quenched and a third being loaded. This involves higher first cost for the mechanical handling equipment but gives a greater output. A consideration of local economics will determine which method of handling is the better.

4.4 WORK STATIONS — GENERAL CONSIDERATION

One frequency may be sufficient for a wide range of components. Therefore, an installation may have one generator unit, with one or more work stations, and a number of interchangeable inductors, each suitable for a particular component.

Each station needs its own independently controlled quench system because quenching is as important as heating. In large installations it is convenient to cool, filter and recirculate the quench water. If the local water is hard it is advantageous to replenish the system with softened water.

Figure 47 illustrates one of two recirculating water pump equipments, part of an installation comprising twenty-four work stations fed from a number of H.F. generators having a total rating of 1,000

Fig. 47. Quench water pumps for large induction heating installation.

kW. Towns water is softened before entering the storage tanks, and cooling plant is incorporated in the recirculating system. 240 gallons of water per minute at a pressure of 120 lb. per sq. inch are used for cooling the inductors, the H.F. transformers and for quench purposes.

Where oil quenching is used the volume must be sufficient not only to ensure adequate quenching but also large enough to avoid the risk of fire. The oil will be circulated and cooling becomes necessary.

4.5 WORK STATION DESIGN

The work station is a productive unit, and upon its design depends the effective use which can be made of the inherent properties of induction heating. Mechanical handling arrangements and the location of the station in relation to other operations have a material effect upon cost and productivity. The selection of a suitable design and layout of work station is therefore very important.

The mechanisms of most work stations can be classified under the following four groups:

a. LONGITUDINAL MOVEMENT. The inductor remains stationary whilst the work is moved either continuously, or intermittently, by

mechanical means such as friction rollers, rotating tables and con-
veyors. Typical components treated continuously are plain circular
bars, rocker arms, and crawler track links.

b. ROTATIONAL MOVEMENT. The inductor remains stationary.
This method is suitable for the treatment of flanged rollers and other
cylindrical parts which cannot be passed through the inductor.

c. INDUCTOR MOVEMENT. The work remains stationary. Heating
of flat surfaces such as lathe beds and the internal surfaces of circular
tubes such as cylinder liners may be treated in this manner.

d. STATIONARY WORKING—in which there is no relative movement between inductor and workpiece.

Sometimes it is necessary to provide combinations of the above.
Details of design vary considerably between manufacturers but the
basic principles are common to them all.

5

Surface hardening:
general engineering applications

5.1 CONTINUOUS HARDENING OF PINS

Carburising and case hardening operations in furnaces are no longer necessary to produce the hard skin and a tough core on component pins such as tractor link pins and gudgeon pins.

Induction heating methods reduce heating costs and labour, conserve floor space and increase productivity. The pins are free from scale and there is a minimum of discolouration. The hardness obtained is the highest possible for the steel concerned while the distortion is lower than that with any other heating method. Grinding after hardening is reduced, and in many cases may be omitted.

The normal method of treating plain pins consists in heating them progressively and passing them through a single-turn inductor and a ring quench. This is represented diagrammatically in Figure 48. Variable speed rollers grip the pins and lower each in turn, one following upon the top of another.

A work station of this type is shown in Figure 49. After passing through the inductor and the quench ring immediately underneath, the bar is gripped between the spring loaded Vee rollers, shown in the lower half of the illustration. The rollers are driven and the speed of travel can be varied according to the depth of hardness required. A common size of plant for this purpose is rated at 100 kW and with this power the speed of feeding varies from 120 inches per minute to 25 inches per minute, depending upon the diameter of the pin and the depth to which the hardening is required. Customary depths lie usually in the range 0.045 in. to 0.200 in. Motor generators operating at 10,000 cycles per second are usual for a plant of this size. If very shallow hardening or a low output is required or the pins are less than $\frac{5}{8}$ in. diameter radio frequencies are recommended.

A typical hardening installation is illustrated in Figure 50. It is customary in production work of this description to check only a small percentage of the pins for surface hardness and to test them for straightness. A hardness testing machine is seen on the left side of the illustration, a machine for testing the straightness, on the right.

5.2 PROGRESSIVE HARDENING OF SHAFTS

5.2 1 AUTOMOBILE BACK AXLES

The physical properties required for automobile back axle shafts have previously been obtained by using alloy steels which were through hardened. This can now be replaced by plain carbon steel hardened by induction methods.

The shafts are hardened free from significant distortion and do not require any subsequent cold straightening. The steel is hardened

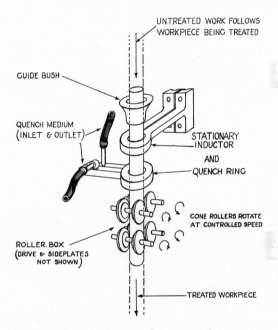

Fig. 48. Schematic diagram of pin station for progressive hardening.

to a depth of approximately $\frac{3}{16}$ in. from the surface and after the subsequent tempering operation has a tensile strength of 90–100 tons/sq. in. The relatively much softer metal in the centre of the shafts (where service stresses are very low) has the effect of retaining considerable residual compressive stresses in the shaft surface, and these have an additional effect in enhancing the fatigue life performance.

Fig. 49. Pin station – inductor quench ring and roller box.

Fig. 50. View of tank track pin hardening installation.

Fig. 51. Automobile back axles – about to be hardened by induction methods.

Fig. 52. Work station for progressive hardening of automobile back axles.

Shafts may be treated by being supported at each end in chucks, collets or centres mounted in crossheads linked together and able to slide in guides.

The shafts shown in Figure 51 are about 30 in. long and 1 in. dia. They are splined at one end and have threads at the other. They are treated in the induction hardening equipment illustrated in Figure 52. The station is supplied from a 125 kW 10 kc motor-driven generator and accommodates two shafts at a time, inserted by hand between spring loaded centres which rotate the shafts whilst they travel downwards through the inductor and quench. The cycle is then entirely automatic and the output is 60 shafts per hour. The station is operated by unskilled labour and is located in the production line. After hardening the shafts are tempered, quenched and finish ground.

5.2 2 AUTOMOBILE ENGINE CAMSHAFTS

Engine camshafts can be hardened very satisfactorily by induction heating. Unhardened zones can be left on the shaft by switching the power off whilst the selected portion of the shaft passes through the inductor.

An installation for hardening camshafts consists of two stations operated alternately, one hardening the cams and the other the bearings. Each station accommodates two camshafts at a time, again supported between sprung centres. After loading and initiating the heating cycle, the two camshafts are automatically raised to the top of the stroke and then lowered until the first cam or bearing is within the inductor. Current is switched on and after the requisite heating time the camshafts are lowered so that the heated section moves from the inductor to the quench and the next section to be heated is then positioned in the inductor. This is repeated until the last section has been heated and quenched and then the camshafts arrive at the unloading position from which they are removed. The machine is then reloaded. The operating cycle of the machine is controlled automatically by a process timer. An installation fed from a 100 kW 10 kc motor generator has a production rate of 80 shafts per hour.

Subject only to the capacity of the high frequency generating plant, there is no limit to the diameter and length of the component which may be heat treated. Depth of hardness may require to be from 0.045 in. to 0.200 in., the operating speed from 12 in. to 100 in. per minute.

Fig. 53. Crankshaft hardening installation. The illustration shows a bank of four crankshaft hardening stations fed from a 200 kW H.F. generator. Each unit has three or four inductors which are simultaneously closed around the selected journals by pneumatic action. Heating and quenching is by the single-shot method.

Generating plant of 100–125 kW capacity is suitable for this type of work.

5.3 ENGINE CRANKSHAFTS

Crankshafts have an improved life when their bearing surfaces are hardened. The customary depths of hardness vary from approximately 0.03 in. up to 0.15 in. Induction heating is particularly well suited to the surface hardening of the bearing surfaces as the heating can be localised in the parts to be treated. Hardened surfaces are free from scale and if there is any distortion it is so slight that it may be corrected by a very light grinding operation. Where the journals are machined to size before hardening, a thin skin–of the order of 0.03 in.–may be adequate for the duty expected. When, however, the journals are ground to size after hardening–a method preferred by many crankshaft manufacturers–then a much thicker skin is

Fig. 54. Crankshaft hardening machine—with rotation of crankshaft. Note the open shaped inductor mounted on the underside of a hinged travelling carriage which permits the heating of all main journals and pin journals at one setting of the shaft. Quenching by submersion in the tank below is carried out automatically after each journal has been heated.

necessary and hardness depth of 0.12 in. to 0.15 in. becomes necessary. The journals may be heated by the single shot method when they are completely enveloped by the inductors, or they may be rotated in the inductors which partially surround them.

In the single shot method, a special split type inductor with a self-contained quench is used. It is clamped around the journal to be treated, electric power is applied and in a few seconds the surface becomes heated. After heating for the requisite time the power is switched off and the quench is turned on. High rates of heating and quenching are necessary to limit the required depth of hardness by preventing undue penetration of heat into the core of the shaft.

With the alternative method a specially shaped inductor is opposed to the journal and the shaft is rotated in the inductor until the whole circumference is heated. After the completion of the heating period the shaft is immersed in the quench medium.

Crankshaft hardening machines have been developed which may be placed in the line of production and operated by unskilled labour. A four-station hardening installation is shown in Figure 53 in which the single shot method is used. Each station has three or four inductors which are closed around the selected journals by pneumatic action. The size of generator required depends on the area of the largest journal to be treated but a 200 kW, 3,000 c/s motor-driven generator is satisfactory for most engines used for road transport; up to 250 journals per hour can be treated. A crankshaft hardening machine embodying heating whilst rotating is shown in Figure 54. The machine is fed from a 220 kW 10,000 cycle motor generator, and crankshafts for agricultural tractors are treated at the rate of 14 per hour. The shafts are 1 per cent Cr. 0.4 per cent C steel forgings. Each is hardened over the surface of five main journals and four crankpin journals, the total area being 125 sq. in. The depth of hardness is approximately 0.10 in. The journals are ground to size after treatment.

R.F. heating may be used to advantage when a thin skin is required. Where a somewhat greater depth of hardness is necessary the heating time may be extended so that a smaller generating plant may be used, involving a lower capital cost for a smaller output.

5.4 ROLLERS AND LINKS FOR CRAWLER TRACKS

Flanged rollers for the crawler tracks of tanks and agricultural vehicles require to be hardened on the tread and the flanges.

An inductor surrounds one half of the tread and flange and the roller is rotated in the inductor to heat the whole circumference (Figure 55). When the heating cycle is completed the roller may be swung on an arm into a quench. A second arm, mechanically coupled to the first, then swings a second roller into the heating position, so that whilst this roller is being heated the previous one is in the quench position. Full use of the high frequency power is thus obtained.

Hardness depths are of the order of $\frac{1}{8}$ in. to $\frac{1}{4}$ in. and roller assemblies with single or double flanges may be treated – sizes ranging from about $6\frac{1}{2}$ in. tread dia. to 9 in. An output of 30 assemblies per hour may be obtained from an H.F. output of 100 kW.

5.5 CRAWLER TRACK LINKS

Crawler track links involve the hardening of flat surfaces. The inductor can be in the form of a hairpin or a gridiron with iron laminations surrounding it, so that the magnetic field is concentrated.

Fig. 55. Station for hardening the tread of tractor crawler track rollers.
Powered by 100 kW H.F. generator 10,000 c.p.s.

A convenient method of handling is to load the links on to a belt conveyor and to pass them under the inductor at a speed of from 12 in. to 24 in. per minute. Several links may be nested together side by side to obtain the greatest output from the power available.

Precautions may be necessary with some designs of links to avoid overheating the feather edges. In such cases it is necessary to harden the links one at a time and to inhibit the overheating of the edges by playing an air mist on them during the hardening operation.

5.6 CYLINDER LINERS

Centrifugally cast cylinder liners can be surface hardened by progressive treatment of the bore. The technique involves the use of specially constructed inductors with which quenching arrangements are incorporated. One type of construction is shown in Figure 56.

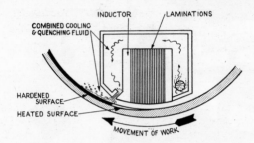

Fig. 56. H.F. progressive hardening of cylindrical surfaces.

The inductor operates on radio frequency of the order of 500,000 cycles per second and power densities of approximately 50 kW per sq. in. can be obtained.

The inductor is mounted inside the bore, and means are provided to permit movement between the inductor and the surface to be hardened. When power is applied the surfaces which pass under the inductor are heated and quenched progressively, resulting in a hardened band the width of the inductor.

Quenching follows the heating as shown in the illustration, and a soft zone may occur due to the reheating of the surface which has already been hardened at the overlap position at the end of the hardening traverse.

Where this is objectionable, however, it is possible to leave an area which is tempered, and not softened. This may be accomplished by using the quenching medium to flood the whole surface of the component whilst it is being heated progressively.

Distortion is extremely small—of the order of o.ooo2 in. on a $4\frac{1}{2}$ in. bore—the risk of cracking is virtually eliminated and power costs are very low. Surface areas may be hardened at the rate of 50 to 60 sq. in. per minute for a power consumption of 1 kWh of R.F.

Fig. 57. H.F. progressive hardening of the inner surface of the bearing ring for the turret track of a fighting vehicle.

Flat cast iron surfaces such as lathe beds can be hardened progressively in a similar manner at speeds up to 2 feet per minute. There is freedom from cracking and a uniform depth of hardness is obtained. Operating costs are low and distortion is negligible.

Another application of progressive hardening is shown in Figure 57. The bearing ring for the turret track of a fighting tank is rotated in front of the inductor which is fed from a 30 kW R.F.

generator. The ring is composed of a 0.40 per cent carbon steel, the hardening temperature is 850°C; the quench medium is a water spray. A hardness of 58 Rockwell C is obtained. The station is semi-automatic and the production rate is one ring per hour. This method of heating is the most convenient for producing the hardness pattern required and there is less distortion and scaling than by any other heating method.

5.7 GEAR TEETH HARDENING

Gears hardened by induction heating are free from serious distortion and the surface finish is such that frequently the gear may be put into service straight from the heat treatment operation. Manufacturing costs are reduced and gear hardening is converted from a series of heating processes into yet another machine tool operation.

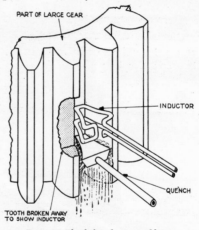

PART OF LARGE GEAR

INDUCTOR

QUENCH

TOOTH BROKEN AWAY
TO SHOW INDUCTOR

Fig. 58. Flank hardening of large
gears by induction heating.

The gear may be contour hardened (a thin case following the exact contour or profile of the teeth) through hardened or flank hardened. The choice of method depends upon the size, material, duty requirements of the gear, and the rate of production desired. Contour hardening involves very high power densities and very short heating times, of the order of a fraction of a second. For example, a 3-inch diameter gear, one inch wide, requires a 300 kW R.F. generator to harden the profile. Radio frequency power requirements can be reduced by pre-heating to about 500°C but a comparatively large generator is still required. Consequently, contour hardening is restricted generally to small parts for which R.F. heating must be used.

Fig. 59. View of an H.F. installation for hardening tractor rear axle final reduction gears.

Fig. 60. The gear (Fig. 59) in position in the inductor.

Fig. 61. A further illustration of the gear hardening installation showing the removal of the gear by gravity after quenching.

5.7 1 THROUGH HARDENING

Through hardening of the teeth is accomplished by surrounding the gear wheel with an inductor and treating by the single shot method. This can be done with lower power densities than for contour hardening. If, however, the pitch is sufficiently great to permit a work coil to embrace one tooth, the single shot method can be used to treat one tooth at a time.

5.7 2 FLANK HARDENING

For large pitches, it is possible for a work coil or an iron core inductor to be placed in the valley between two teeth, thus heating two flanks at a time. High power generator equipment is not required but the total heat treatment time is prolonged. This can be done by the single shot method, or by the progressive method (as illustrated in Figure 58) for very wide gears. Thus, large generating equipment is not required but the total heat treatment time for the whole component is prolonged.

5.8 APPLICATIONS

A general view of an installation for through hardening the teeth of the final reduction gear for the rear axle of a tractor is shown in Figure 59. The gears which are machined from one-piece forgings pass along the production line up to the hardening machine, where they are loaded into the inductor (Figure 60).

When the teeth are heated the gear is oil-quenched by submerging it in the quench tank underneath. After quenching, a bogie elevates it to the position shown in Figure 61 whence it is conveyed over gravity rollers back on to the production line. The hardening machine is fed from a 150 kW motor generator at 10,000 c.p.s. and an output of 60 gears per hour is obtained.

The close up of another gear hardening machine (Figure 62) shows the final drive gear ring for an agricultural tractor. It is in position on a transfer loading platform and is about to be lifted by the manipulating ram. The first motion is for the gear to be raised into the inductor and the loading platform withdrawn. The power

Fig. 62. Work station for H.F. hardening bull gear rings. The untreated gear has been placed on the loading platform, to be lifted by the manipulator arm into the inductor.

77

is then switched on and at the end of the heating time the gear is submerged in the quenching oil. The gear ring is rotated during heating and quenching.

The oil is maintained at constant temperature by means of a heat exchanger and a circulating pump.

The machine is fully automatic and an extremely difficult gear hardening operation is carried out expeditiously and with the utmost precision entirely with unskilled labour.

The output of the machine is 30 gear rings per hour and the rating of the generator is 150 kW. A frequency of 10,000 c.p.s. is used.

6

Surface hardening:
light engineering applications

6.1 GENERAL

Induction heating can be used with very great advantage for the surface hardening of a variety of small components which require less power than the samples already cited. Where the dimensions are small R.F. power becomes necessary.

For small outputs a hand loading fixture with automatic time control of the heating cycle is sufficiently satisfactory. It can be observed from the illustrations that the inductor and the mechanism associated with it is so simple that it is possible for this apparatus to be constructed by the user to suit the particular component. Where large scale production is required, however, completely mechanised equipments are preferable.

The close control of induction heating together with its cleanliness, safety and simplicity, makes it very suitable for repetition work needing only unskilled labour. The equipment can be installed in the line of production for that component, thereby reducing unnecessary transport and other operational costs.

6.2 PRODUCTION DATA

The following production data is representative. Each example relates to an R.F. installation. The cost of power drawn from the mains is based on electricity at 1d per unit. This is negligibly small compared with the total cost of the part.

TABLE 4. Surface hardening – production data.

EXAMPLE 1 *Product: Contact Breaker Cam*

Dimensions	Cam 0.75 in. dia. × 0.5 in. width
Material	Low carbon steel (carburised)
Process	Harden cam surface
Production	300 per hour
Handling	Automatic indexing table: hand loading and discharge
Power cost	Approx. 0.06d per piece

EXAMPLE 2 *Product: Refrigerator Compressor Crank*

Dimensions   Crank pin 1.4 in. dia. × 0.75 in. width

Material   0.40 per cent carbon direct-hardening steel

Process   Harden the surface of the crank pin

Production   350 per hour

Handling   Manual jig: automatic timing of heating and quenching.

Power cost   Approx. 0.13d per piece

EXAMPLE 3 *Product: Ignition Distributor Shaft*

Dimensions   0.5 in. dia. × 7.0 in. long

Material   0.40 per cent carbon direct-hardening steel

Process   Surface harden a 5.0 in. length of the 0.5 in. dia. shaft

Production   450 per hour

Handling   Vertical, automatic feed with rotation of shaft: hand loading

Power cost   Approx. 0.1d per piece

EXAMPLE 4 *Product: Starter Ring Gears*

Material   0.4 per cent carbon direct-hardening steel

Process   Harden the teeth

Production   100–150 per hour, depending upon the size of the ring

Handling   Automatic timing of heating and quench; unskilled labour

Power cost   Approx. 0.4d to 0.6d per ring

EXAMPLE 5 *Product: Chain Saw Teeth*

Material   Direct hardening steel

Process   Hardening face of teeth

Production   700 per hour

Handling   Manual loading and automatic ejection

Power cost   Approx. 0.03d per tooth

EXAMPLE 6 *Product: Tappet Screws*

Material   0.55 per cent carbon direct-hardening steel

Process   Harden. Oil quench

Production   1,450 per hour

Handling   Turntable. Manual loading and auto ejection

Power cost   Approx. 0.01d per piece

Fig. 63. General purpose radio frequency generator for induction heating.
Output 25 kWs.

EXAMPLE 7 *Product: Rocker Arm*

Material	Low carbon steel (carburised)
Process	Surface harden the pad
Production	350 per hour
Handling	Indexing turntable. Manual loading and unloading
Power cost	Approx. 0.04d per pad

6.3 GENERAL PURPOSE APPLICATIONS

The 25 kW valve generator illustrated in Figure 63 is the source of
R.F. power for an installation which handles many applications,
most of them of an intermittent nature. The simple work stations
and fixtures seen on the bench in the foreground may be adapted or
developed to suit changing requirements. The method of treating

F

Fig. 64. Selective heating – a simple form of work station.

a shaft, leaving both ends soft, is shown in Figure 64. Because of the small number, no mechanical method of holding is used. Again the treatment of small numbers of ratchet racks can be carried out in the very simple inductor shown in Figure 65. The rack is made of mild steel. After carburising treatment it is hardened on the teeth of the ratchet only.

Localised hardening of very small components can present many difficult problems, but the heating of the ends of grub screws by R.F. induction, as shown in Figure 66, can be a very simple solution. Manual operation is very satisfactory.

6.4 R.F. HEATING OF INTERNAL COMBUSTION ENGINE PARTS

6.4 1 ROCKER ARMS

Selective hardening of the wearing surfaces only, can be obtained by induction heating. The simplest possible method of handling small batches of rocker arms for hardening the pads is shown in Figure 67. A high rate of production is obtainable on account of the short heating time. The operator needs no special protective clothing and the work

Fig. 65. Heating a carburised steel component for selective hardening.

Fig. 66. Simple work station for heating the ends of small components – for subsequent quenching for hardening.

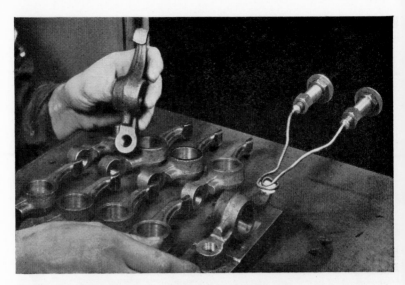

Fig. 67. A simple hand operation – heating the pads of rocker arms for hardening.

Fig. 68. R.F. heat treatment machine for the large production of hardened rocker arm pads. 9 kW generator. Production rate 375 rocker arms per hour.

coil need not be guarded, as there are no dangerous high voltages. A double-wound transformer is used to isolate the inductor from the high voltage R.F. system. The supply is drawn from a 5 kW R.F. generator.

The large scale production of rocker arms necessitates the use of a rotating table shown in Figure 68. The operator is shown loading the rocker arms on to the work table which has an intermittent motion in a clockwise direction. The components move under a pancake coil where they are heated, and then to the quenching position. The rocker arms are finally unloaded automatically into a discharge chute. The station is supplied from a 9 kW R.F. generator and has a production rate of 375 rocker arms per hour.

6.4 2 ROCKER SHAFTS

R.F. heating can be used with success to harden the bearing surfaces of rocker shafts. The work station illustrated in Figure 69 fed from a 50 kW R.F. generator has a production rate of approximately 90 shafts per hour. The shafts are progressed intermittently through the inductor and quench, heating and quenching occurring only over the selected parts. A clear view of the component and the inductor and quench ring of another installation is shown in Figure 70, the component being a diesel injector pump camshaft.

6.4 3 HARDENING OF VALVE STEMS

A 5 kW R.F. generator is shown in Figure 71 for hardening the ends of valve stems at the rate of 2,000 per hour.

The valves are placed in position by hand, and the operator initiates the heating cycle which is terminated automatically. At the end of the heating time the valve stems are plunged into the quenching water.

6.4 4 HARDENING THE SEATS OF ALLOY STEEL VALVES

A method of hardening the seats of alloy steel valves is shown in Figure 72. The valves are held magnetically in the jig until the valve seat is heated to the correct temperature, when the power is automatically cut off. The solenoid releases the valve which drops into a water quench. Operated from a 25 kW R.F. generator, the speed of treatment is several hundred per hour.

6.5 COMPONENTS FOR DOMESTIC APPLIANCES

The R.F. induction heater illustrated in Figure 73 is used to sur-face harden worm gears at each end of shafts.

The shaft is inserted in the machine, one end being heated and

Fig. 69. Selective hardening of the bearing surfaces of I.C.E. rocker shafts. R.F. generator 50 kW. Output 90 shafts per hour.

Fig. 70. Inductor and quench ring of an installation for hardening camshafts.

Fig. 71. Hardening the ends of valve stems by radio frequency heating.

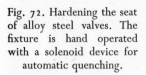

Fig. 72. Hardening the seat of alloy steel valves. The fixture is hand operated with a solenoid device for automatic quenching.

Fig. 73. Hardening worm gears at the ends of shafts by radio frequency.

Fig. 74. Worm shaft bent to demonstrate the soft core inside the case after induction hardening.

oil quenched automatically. The other end is treated similarly. The operator has merely to load and unload. The sample shown in the upper part of Figure 74 has been bent to demonstrate the soft and tough core inside the hardened skin.

6.6 LAWN-MOWER CUTTER BLADES

The localised effect of R.F. heating can be applied to the hardening of lawn-mower cutter blades and cylinders. The station shown in Figure 75 is fully automatic and after loading the machine the operator closes the door and the hardening cycle commences. In the case of cylinder cutters the five or six blades are hardened automatically in sequence. The inductor and quench can be seen below the fixture which holds the cylinder in position.

The station is fed from a 30 kW 450 kc. R.F. valve generator.

Fig. 75. Fully automatic R.F. installation for hardening lawn-mower cutter blades and cylinders.

Fig. 76. R.F. station for hardening passenger vehicle starter-ring gears. 25 kW generator. Production 55-120 gears per hour.

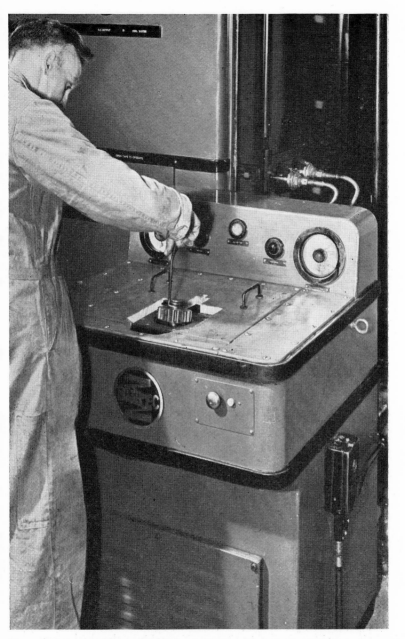

Fig. 77. General purpose, single-shot induction hardening unit, shown in use for hardening gearbox pinions.

91

Fig. 78. Shrinking and hardening automobile starter ring gears. R.F. generator 25 kW output. Process time 60-85 seconds depending on the size of the flywheel.

6.7 GEAR TEETH HARDENING

Small gear wheels and pinions may be hardened very satisfactorily by means of R.F. heating. The single shot method of heating is usual.

The machine shown in Figure 77 is equipped with a 25 kW R.F. generator and is capable of treating pinions up to approximately 5 ins. diameter at the rate of 50 per hour, or more for smaller sizes.

The surfaces of small teeth such as those on automobile starter ring gears can be hardened selectively, leaving the inner part of the ring soft. The unit illustrated in Figure 76 is fed from a 25 kW R.F. generator and the output is 55 to 120 gears per hour, dependent on size. After heating, the gear is quenched automatically with water at a controlled temperature. No cleaning is required after treatment, and consistent results are obtained, using unskilled labour.

The machine shown in Figure 78 combines the dual purpose of hardening starter-ring gear teeth and shrinking the ring on to the

92

flywheel. The two operations are carried out simultaneously with resultant saving in labour, time, and electricity. The installation consists of a 25 kW R.F. generator in conjunction with a two-station change-over switch, which energises two multi-turn inductors alternately. The coils are mounted on top of the quenching tank which is fitted with two vertical shafts capable of rotation and up and down movement. The shafts work alternately, so that while the assembly on one side is heating, the assembly on the other side is quenching.

The cycle of operations is as follows:

1. The shafts rise to loading position, which is slightly above the level of the inductor, and the flywheel is placed on the support with the starter ring gear positioned on top and held by a spider, which ensures that the ring gear remains level during its movement on to the seating of the flywheel.

2. The operation is started by push button, the shaft is rotated at about 60 r.p.m. and drops to the heating position as the inductor is energised. The starter ring then expands and drops on to the seating under gravity. The heating continues until the teeth attain a temperature of about 850°C.

3. The shaft then drops to the quenching level, the rotation continuing, and remains there until the completion of the heating of the assembly on the other shaft. The first shaft then emerges with the treated flywheel assembly from the oil, for unloading and reloading.

The heating time varies from 60 to 85 seconds dependent on the size of the flywheel.

7

Through heating

7.1 TYPICAL APPLICATIONS

1. Heating of slugs–ferrous and non-ferrous.
2. Heating of billets–ferrous and non-ferrous.
3. Heating of bar ends for upsetting and upset forging.
4. Heating of tube ends for flanging and nosing.
5. Continuous heating of bar for shearing and forging, e.g. manufacture of nuts and mine-drill bits.
6. Heating of bolt blanks for heading.

The need at the present time is for increased rate of production, reduction of waste and congenial working conditions. Recruitment of labour for work under conditions tolerated by their forefathers is becoming increasingly difficult. The conditions in some of the old forge shops for example are amongst the worst in the metal-working industry. They are conducive neither to good craftsmanship nor to increased production, but the installation of induction heating with its associated cleanliness and absence of waste heat can ameliorate appreciably the poor working conditions and provide an incentive to greater productivity.

The main advantages of induction heating in the forge shop may be summarised as:

1. Improved operating conditions due to absence of waste heat and fumes.
2. Instant starting without long warming-up periods.
3. Small floor space.
4. Uniformity of temperature.
5. Scale almost entirely eliminated due to rapid rate of heating.
6. Increased die life resulting from (4) and (5).
7. Mechanical handling, which reduces labour costs.
8. Use of unskilled labour.
9. Low maintenance costs.

7.2 HEATING FOR FORGING

Forging can be commenced within a few minutes of starting up. A long period of preheating–as is essential with fuel fired furnaces–is unnecessary, and power is not consumed during non-working periods. This quick starting and stopping results in a great economy

Fig. 79. Through heating for bending. Simple type of work station.

of power, and induction heating for forging can show savings even on the cost of heating alone.

A consumption of about 0.2 kWh H.F. per lb. of steel heated to about 1,200°C may be expected. The power requirements for forging are, of course, dependent on the weight of the steel per hour to be heated, and may be from ten to several hundred kilowatts for each heater unit. Motor generators are at present the most suitable means of supplying large amounts of power, and they are available for outputs of up to 2,500 kW and at frequencies from 500 to 10,000 c/s. This range of frequency is suitable for heating any size of work from about $\frac{1}{2}$ in. to 6 in. dia. or square. Radio frequency heating is necessary for material of smaller cross section. Normal mains frequency heating, for heating for forging and the

Fig 80. Through heating for forging. General view of a modern forging press shop.

Fig. 81. Continuous type billet heater and press.

extrusion of large billets of non-ferrous materials has already been referred to in Chapter 3.

Equipment for induction heating for forging may be of a simple type, hand operated or completely mechanised. A very simple fixture is shown in Figure 79. The inductor is fed from a $7\frac{1}{2}$ kW R.F. generator. Bar stock is being heated locally to be cranked for subsequent manufacture into motor car starting handles.

Fig. 82. Two-station automatic billet heater feeding a forging press.

7.3 BILLET HEATING

A general view of part of a modern mechanical press forging shop producing automobile components is shown in Figure 80. The presses are fed from induction heaters equipped with mechanical handling to provide a continuous supply of billets. The billets are loaded

G

Fig. 83. Nine-station billet heater with automatic feeding arrangements for forging shell blanks.

by hand on to the continuously rotating table of the heater, from the stillages in the foreground of Figure 81. The heated billets are automatically discharged down the chute to the press operator.

The total installation consists of 12 heaters giving a gross output of some 8 tons per hour. The high frequency motor generator equipment totals approximately 3,500 kW.

A station for heating small billets usually comprises a helical coil through which the billets are pushed by a pneumatic cylinder from a charging magazine. A chute delivers the hot billets to the press operator.

A two coil billet heater of this type is shown in Figure 82. It has a loading magazine and pusher type feeder mechanism for handling billets from $1\frac{1}{2}$ ins. to 4 ins. Different sizes of interchangeable coils are required for different sizes of billets. The output is 1,000 lbs. per hour with a 200 kW motor generator unit.

A nine coil billet heater shown in Figure 83 is another example of mechanical handling in the forge shop. The photograph, taken from the discharge side of the heater, shows only one of the nine coil boxes assembled on it.

98

The heater station is supplied from a 750 kW 1,500 cycle motor generator. The billets, weighing 44 lb. each are unloaded from an overhead conveyor on to a platform behind the coils. The billets are placed in position, in sequence, and are pushed into the coils by a mechanical charger. At the end of the heating period for any particular billet, the coil is tilted automatically to discharge the billet down a chute, to the press operator. The coils are arranged around the sector of a circle so that all the billets are discharged to a focal point. The output is 90 billets per hour.

7.4 CONTROL OF HEAT FOR FORGING

The heating operation is based upon the control of time and power input. The heating time is determined by the speed of the feeding mechanism and the power input is determined by the generator voltage. Both of these are thereafter automatically controlled to a constant level, so that the billets are uniformly supplied to the press at the same temperature and at a constant rate.

The effect of frequency on billet size and heating time is shown in the following table :

TABLE 5. Heating time in minutes to raise the temperature of steel billet to 1,150°C

Frequency Cycles per second	Diameter of Billet in inches							
	1	2	3	4	5	6	7	8
50	—	—	—	—	3	4.5	6	7.5
1,000	—	1.5	3.0	5.5	9	—	—	—
3,000	0.5	1.7	3.8	7.0	—	—	—	—
10,000	0.6	2.2	5.0	9.0	—	—	—	—

For the heating of steel billets dual frequency heaters can be used. L.F. power is employed for heating billets smaller than 4 or 5 ins. in diameter up to the magnetic change point, as it is efficient up to this stage. The final heating to forging temperature follows immediately by the billet passing into a separate coil supplied with H.F. power. This permits the rating of the H.F. generator to be reduced—frequently to less than half. Consequently the capital cost of the installation is very much lower than if the whole of the heating were done by high frequency.

7.5 HEATING OF BAR ENDS FOR MAKING FORGINGS

The majority of heating requirements involve the heating of the ends of partially hot bars. The bars are initially several feet long and the end few inches being forged and removed at each operation.

Fig. 84. Heating the ends of bars before upsetting.

Fig. 85. Automatic upsetting press for automobile stabiliser bars. View of one of the induction heaters.

The temperature of the end of the bar which remains is determined by the actual length which has been heated, the length which has been removed and the time taken before the next heating operation commences. The bars eventually become too short to be used and must be replaced by cold ones, which will then require a much longer heating time than the partially hot bars. This complicates the heating problem, and one of the ways of overcoming it has been adopted on the heater shown in Figure 84. The cold bars are preheated by the unit on the left and are then inserted in the 3-coil heater. A 30 kW 10 kc motor generator gives an output of 125 operations per hour, each operation being the through heating of a 10 in. length of $\frac{7}{8}$ in. dia. bar.

An automatic upsetting press for automobile stabiliser bars is illustrated in Figures 85 and 86. Ground bars, approximately 6 ft. 0 in. in length and $\frac{5}{8}$ in. in dia. are heated and upset to form spherical portions towards the ends of the bars, for linking them to the track control arms. R.F. induction heating is used.

After the bar has been hand-loaded into the Vee-grooves of two supporting arms it is clamped into position and the cycle of operations is initiated by pressing a switch. Immediately two induction heating coils move into position and the R.F. power is switched on. The bar is heated in about 30 seconds to the upsetting temperature of approximately 1,100°C over a length of $2\frac{1}{2}$ to 3 inches at a short distance from each end. When heating has been completed, the R.F. heating coils move back rapidly and the bar is carried downwards to the upsetting position. Immediately it is in position the bar is clamped and the dies close simultaneously at each end. After upsetting, the dies open and the bar is raised to the original loading position. A close-up view of one end of the machine at the completion of the operating cycle, showing the shape of one end of the upset bar, is shown in Figure 85.

Fed from the 15 kW R.F. generator shown behind the machine in Figure 86, approximately 60 bars per hour can be turned out.

The machine, which forms part of a self-contained production line is fully automatic and is operated by unskilled labour.

7.6 HEATING OF PINS FOR BOLT HEADING

An automatic machine for heating the ends of bolt blanks prior to the heading operation is shown in Figure 87.

The machine can accommodate bolt blanks from 10 to 28 mm. in diameter and up to 12 in. in length. Only the length which is

Fig. 86. Automatic upsetting press for automobile stabiliser bars. General view of the installation.

necessary to form the head is heated. The machine illustrated is one of a two-station installation which is fed from a 150 kW 10 kc motor generator.

Typical operating results for three sizes of pins, obtained from 60 kW induction heaters working well within their capacity, are given in Table 6. The heater occupies a floor space of only 4 feet × 3 feet.

TABLE 6. Heating of pins for bolt heading

Diameter of pin	$\frac{3}{4}$ in.	$\frac{5}{8}$ in.	$\frac{1}{2}$ in.
Heated length	$2\frac{1}{2}$ in.	$2\frac{1}{2}$ in.	$2\frac{1}{2}$ in.
Temperature on ejection	1,250°C	1,250°C	1,250°C
Output per hour	1,053	1,360	1,080
High-frequency power loading	60 kW	50 kW	42 kW
Type of forging	Single-blow	Single-blow	Double-blow

102

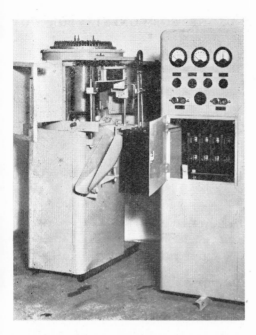

Fig. 87. Station for heating the ends of bolt blanks before heading.

Fig. 88. Vertical three-station automatic equipment for heating the ends of components for hot forming. The operator is seen removing a heated component.

7.7 HEATING THE ENDS OF COMPONENTS FOR HOT FORMING

Shell nosing is carried out by induction heating and production data is given below:

TABLE 7. Shell nosing: typical operating results

Shell diameter	105 mm.		120 mm.		155 mm.	
High frequency Power loading (kW)	200	300	200	300	200	300
Hourly production	100	150	80	120	35	55
Heated length (in.)	8	8	8	8	14	14

A vertical three-station automatic equipment for heating the ends of components for hot forming is shown in Figure 88. Fed from a 100 kW motor generator, an output of 50/100 pieces per hour is obtained, according to size.

8

Annealing

Including tempering,
normalising, stress relieving and drawing

8.1 GENERAL

A hardened steel may be brittle and therefore unable to withstand
mechanical shock. To overcome this, steel is subjected to a tempering process. High carbon steels are tempered at temperatures about
200°C to 300°C. The original hardness of the steel is not greatly
decreased, but the brittleness will be lessened owing to the equali-
sing of internal strains which have accrued during hardening.

Tool steels are tempered at higher temperatures–up to about
650°C. The original hardness is reduced but ductility and toughness
of the steel is greatly improved. When this treatment is applied to
medium carbon steel a tough and strong material is produced capable of withstanding sudden shock and having a good fatigue life.

ANNEALING is a process of heating steel and other metals to a
definite temperature for a definite time and then cooling at a suitable
rate. The treatment induces softness in the metal and improves its
machinability and cold working properties. It also frees the metal
from internal stresses which may have been set up in it by a previous
manipulation.

The NORMALISING of steel involves heating it to a higher temperature than for annealing and then permitting it to cool naturally
in air. The process is sometimes referred to as grain refining. It ren-
ders the structure of the metal more uniform and improves the
mechanical properties.

Bars which have been rolled and then emerge from the mill at a
comparatively low temperature lose much of their ductility which
can then be restored by normalising.

STRESS RELIEVING is a heating process which is carried out at
a temperature generally lower than that required for annealing or
normalising. The sole purpose is to release internal stresses such as
occur due to machining, casting, hot forming, irregular cooling or
welding.

Induction heating can be used to advantage for all these processes

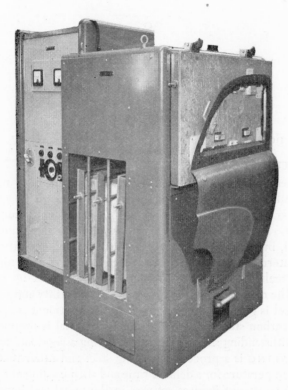

Fig. 89. Selective heating for annealing.

in many instances owing to the ease with which it can be applied, its cleanliness, its quick availability and easy adaptation to special requirements.

8.2 TEMPERING

The induction tempering of steel saves time. For example 1 in. diameter bars can be tempered in one minute compared with a half-an-hour or more which would be required by ordinary furnace heating.

Steel bar stock can be hardened and tempered in a continuous process on a single machine using induction heating. A uniform and tough material is obtained in a scale-free form suitable for machining into high-quality components. The hardness penetration can be controlled so that a relatively soft core can be left for subsequent removal by drilling or by machining to produce, for example, components such as nuts from hexagon bars where the hardness is required only through the wall of the finished article.

8.3 ANNEALING

Induction annealing has the advantage that it can be localised in selected parts of the object. For example, annealing is required between successive pressing operations in the manufacture of automobile doors. Induction heating equipment illustrated in Figure 89 shows how heating is restricted to the corners of the doors. With conventional methods a very considerable portion would have to be heated with a consequent waste of power and with the risk of distortion. The work is heated in about 20 seconds by means of four 'pancake' coils connected in series and supplied by an R.F. generator rated at 7 kW. The process is semi-automatic and the machine has an output of 120 doors an hour.

The annealing of the ends of shafts made from mild steel which has been carburised is shown in Figure 90. The process can be

Fig. 90. Heating the ends of shafts for annealing.

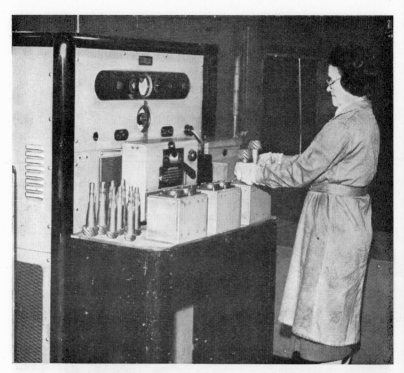

Fig. 91. Annealing automobile rear axle driving pinions.

carried out in the production line. Localised annealing is obtained with a minimum of scale. The machine can deal with 200 shafts an hour, the R.F. generator being rated at 2¾ kW.

The annealing of rear axle driving pinions is shown in Figure 91.

The component, made from a low carbon mild steel, is fully machined except for the threading of the shaft end, and is then carburised. The shaft end must then be annealed to obtain the required physical properties. Selective heating by R.F. induction enables this to be carried out in the direct line of production.

Three sizes of shafts are treated in pairs, one pair at a time. They are inserted by hand into the appropriate inductors and the operator depresses either a foot switch or a push button. This initiates the heating cycle which is controlled automatically by a process timer. At the end of the cycle the operator removes the components which are placed in a storage receptacle and allowed to cool slowly. Fed from a 6 kW 400,000 c/s R.F. generator an output of 370 components per hour is obtained.

Fig. 92. Induction heating for stress relieving.

Fig. 93. Stress relieving small components by induction heating.

8.4 STRESS RELIEVING of large components by normal frequency induction heating has been referred to in Chapter 3. Practical experience has shown that high-frequency induction heating is often preferable in spite of the capital cost being somewhat higher. The high-frequency power is much more flexible owing to the greater range over which it can be controlled and the greater ease of obtaining a sufficiently high power density. The lower current in the inductor enables smaller cables to be used. They are easier to handle and can be applied more readily to the component.

The use of high-frequency power for stress relieving is illustrated in Figure 92. This shows a part of one of the heat exchangers for a nuclear-energy power station. The heat exchanger is built from a number of steel cylinders welded together and finally closed by having domed ends welded to them. The edges of the sections to be welded together can be preheated inductively before welding and when the welding operation is finished the whole of the affected area can be inductively heated to the temperature required for stress relieving. The parts to be heated are covered with asbestos on the outside and flexible cables of a special construction are laid in place to form the inductor. Asbestos is then applied to the outside of these to form the heat insulation which is held in place by non-ferrous plates clamped to the cylinders. Similar asbestos lagging is applied to the inside of the parts to be heated. The ends of the cables are taken through boxes in the floor and there connected to busbars which are supplied from the 200 kW 2,500 cycle generating plant.

The use of induction heating for stress relieving and annealing is not confined to large-scale operation, but can equally well be applied to small components.

Local stress relieving of tractor pins which have previously been furnace-hardened can be carried out on the machine illustrated in Figure 93. This machine has a continuous chain conveying mechanism for the pins and a production rate of 720 pins an hour.

9

Brazing, soldering and welding

9.1 GENERAL

Brazing and soldering by induction heating can be one of the quickest and cleanest methods of joining metals together. The application should however, be carefully examined, as in these operations more than in any other, it is often beneficial to re-design the parts so that the fullest advantage can be taken of Induction Heating.

9.2 BRAZING

The aim is to localise the heat at the joint area to bring the joint surface uniformly to a temperature slightly higher than the flow point of the brazing alloy, and to allow time for the alloy to flow and fill the interstices of the joint. The inductor coil must be designed to heat all faces of the joint—which are not necessarily symmetrical—at such a rate that shielded areas attain a simultaneous temperature rise by heat conduction. Sometimes the shape of the coil may be simplified by changes in design of the part.

In all applications of induction brazing it is usual to employ shaped pieces of brazing material. The brazing material and the flux is applied to the assembly which is then heated. It may be advantageous to re-design the part so that the brazing metal is retained in position. When the part is heated the brazing material melts and flows immediately into the joint, without appreciable scale or extensive discoloration occurring on the outside. Jets of suitably prepared gases may be directed to envelop the joint to give complete freedom from discoloration. For some metals, such as stainless steel, a fully protective atmosphere is necessary. The component and the inductor can then be located in an enclosure to which the atmosphere can be applied.

Should it be necessary, however, to heat the whole of the component, as, for example, one of complex shape having many joints, it would then be preferable to use an electric resistance-heating furnace to which a controlled atmosphere could also be supplied. In these circumstances furnace heating could prove more economical particularly when the component is large.

Induction brazing enables large rates of output to be obtained; therefore suitable mechanical handling and jigging arrangements become necessary, which permit the use of unskilled labour. For most purposes only a small amount of power is required and this may be provided most economically by an R.F. generator. With clean components and an ample coating of flux the operation is extremely simple.

9.2 1 BRAZING APPLICATIONS

Carbide inserts for tools
Tips for rock drills
Shanks for twist drills
Joints for automobile shock absorbers
Petrol filler assemblies
Parts for universal joints

Modern practice tends towards the use of silver solders for the brazing of *carbide* tips for cutting tools, drills and saws of every type. Induction heating provides a quick, clean and convenient method of applying heat to the part which has to be brazed because the heat can be localised in that area.

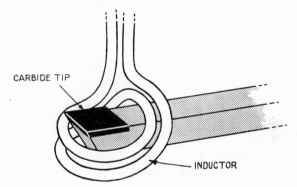

Fig. 94. H.F. heating for brazing tungsten carbide tool tips.

When the tool has been prepared it is placed in position within the heating coil (Figure 94) which may be handled safely during the brazing operation, as it operates at an extremely low voltage. The positioning of the work within the coil is not critical, the most suitable position being quickly observed.

Spacing pieces of copper gauze, or of copper coated with silver solder, are frequently inserted between the tip and the stock to make the tool more resistant to impact when in service. It is customary to place the tool in a bed of hot sand immediately after brazing, to allow it to cool without cracking.

H   113

Fig. 95. An installation for brazing tungsten carbide tips to a wide range of machine tools.

A 5 kW R.F. installation for brazing carbide tips to a wide range of tool shanks is illustrated in Figure 95. The tip is held in position until the brazing metal sets; meanwhile another assembly is heated in the coil. Carbide tips, $\frac{5}{8}$ in. × $\frac{1}{4}$ in. × $\frac{1}{8}$ in. are brazed to $\frac{5}{8}$ in. square steel shanks in 25 seconds.

Twist drill manufacture sometimes requires the brazing of straight bodies into tapered shanks. The operation can become entirely unskilled when R.F. heating is used.

A mixture of powdered silver solder and flux is applied to the bore of the shank which is located in a simple type of work station

Fig. 96. Brazing components of turbine blades.

fixture. The heating cycle is initiated and when the brazing material is molten, the operator inserts the drill body into the bore of the shank. At the end of the heating cycle, which is controlled automatically by a process timer, the power is cut off and the assembled drill is removed to be quenched in oil. Fed from a 2 kW R.F. generator the average process time for drills up to 17/64 in. diameter is about 14 seconds.

A similar application on a much larger scale relates to the brazing of packing pieces to turbine blades (Figure 96). Due to the speed with which heat may be generated in the parts, the braze is made

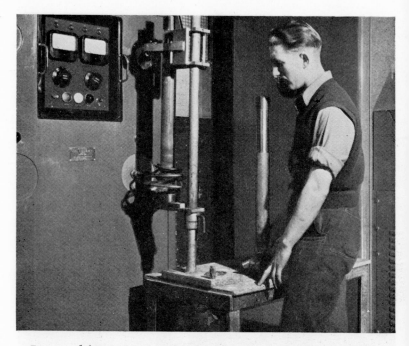

Fig. 97. 7½ kW R.F. generator and work station for heating for brazing.

without distorting the component, while the formation of scale is negligible.

R.F. heating can be used advantageously in many of the brazing applications which occur in the engineering industries, but as has been explained, suitable jigging and handling arrangements must be used to obtain full benefit from the high speed of heating.

The steering column assemblies of heavy transport vehicles may be brazed in a simple hand loaded fixture as shown in Figure 97, but for the brazing, for example, of drain plug bosses into the sheet metal sumps of automobile engines some form of jigging and mechanical handling is very necessary. One method of carrying this out is illustrated in Figure 98. The sumps are registered on supporting fixtures, mounted on a rotating table. Whilst one sump is being loaded the other is undergoing treatment. In another arrangement a power operated table may be lowered for loading purposes and raised to bring the work into the field of the inductor. When the shape permits, gases to provide a protective atmosphere may be passed through the assembly to prevent oxidation.

A fixture, illustrating the induction brazing of radio valve components in a controlled atmosphere is shown in Figure 101. A copper plated ring of mild steel is being brazed to a ring of Nilo K. The parts of the assembly are shown separately on the work table, together with a ring of the eutectic alloy solder (melting point 778°C) used.

The component parts of cylindrical containers shown in Figure 99 can be silver-soldered conveniently on a rotating table on which they are loaded by hand and then passed in pairs under the inductor, illustrated in Figure 100. The inductor is fed from a 6 kW R.F. generator.

When induction heating methods are adopted, brazing the fittings to petrol tanks can become a job on the production line with the use of unskilled labour only.

Drain plugs and petrol unions are brazed into petrol tanks at the

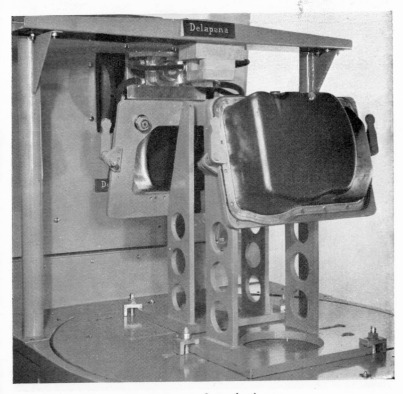

Fig. 98. Brazing drain plug bosses.

Fig. 99. Component parts of cylindrical containers, prepared for silver soldering.

Fig. 100. Rotating table fixture for silver soldering cylindrical containers.

Fig. 101. Brazing radio valve components by R.F. heating.

rate of two drain plugs or petrol unions in 18 seconds on the installation shown in Figure 102. The two-position work table is fed
from a 10 kW R.F. generator. Filler plugs and petrol tanks shown
in Figure 103 are brazed at the rate of one tank in 22 seconds, when
fed from a 5 kW R.F. generator.

9.3 SOLDERING

Soft soldering is a low temperature operation–below 500°C–and it
might be thought that relatively costly induction heating plant would

Fig. 102. An installation for brazing petrol tank assemblies.

Fig. 103. Work station and handling fixture for brazing petrol tank filler plug bosses.

have no industrial value in this field. On the contrary, the ability of induction heating to concentrate heat either on the surface of the work or on a longitudinal section, together with its high speed of working makes it an excellent method for production work.

It is almost unbelievably fast when compared with soldering irons, blow lamps, or torches. It avoids the disfiguring marks of the electrodes used in the direct resistance-heating method. It eliminates scaling and heat is not wasted. Better and cheaper articles may be produced by unskilled labour, using induction soldering than are obtained by skilled labour using other methods.

A 6 kW R.F. induction heater, designed for general purpose soldering and brazing is shown in Figure 104. With two or three different heating coils a wide range of components may be handled. When used in conjunction with a radio frequency step-down transformer, the coils are completely safe and can be handled during the soldering or brazing operations without risk of shock or burns.

Induction soldering can be carried out with the utmost precision but as in the case of brazing the fit of the component is important. Maximum clearances between the parts should not exceed 0.005 in. in the joining of similar metals, and the better the fit between the parts the better the joint will be.

9.3 1 SOLDERING APPLICATIONS

Mild steel pressings are soldered with precision on the induction heater station shown in Figure 105. This station, built with the accuracy of a machine tool, has an indexing rotating table on to which the pressings are fed. The production rate is about 600 assemblies per hour.

An example of precision assembly, combined with a high rate of production, is illustrated in Figure 106. Petrol lighter cases are suspended from a table which is driven at a constant speed. The assemblies, with the solder applied to them, pass between the sides of a long hairpin inductor and are heated uniformly for a time which is sufficient to ensure that the solder penetrates into the joint. Continuing the circuit they cool freely in air and are not disturbed mechanically until the solder has solidified. The production rate is 1,000 lighters per hour.

The turntable fixture shown in Figure 107 is for soldering the bracket on to the body of automobile ignition system condensers. As in the previous example the components pass under a long hairpin inductor, which is shown in the illustration.

The soldering of spouts and bases on to kettles, using a gas flame,

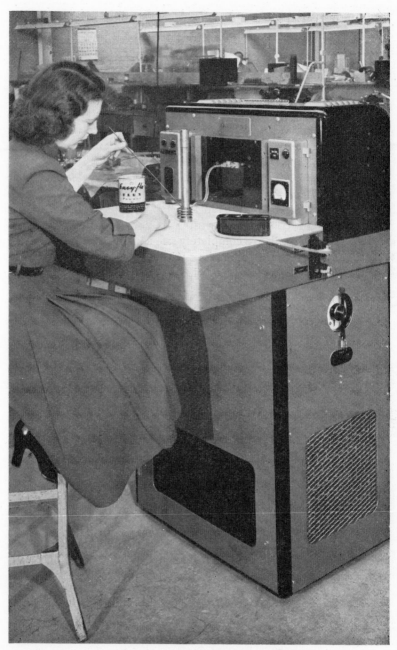

Fig. 104. A general-purpose workshop soldering and brazing machine.

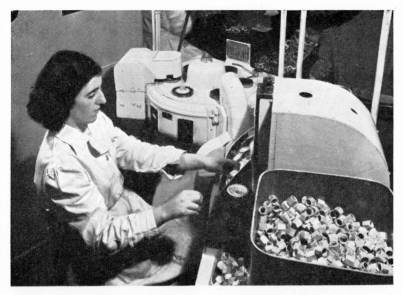

Fig. 105. Work station with indexing rotating table for soldering and brazing.

Fig. 106. Rotating table fixture for soldering petrol lighter cases.

Fig. 107. Turntable fixture for soldering components.

Fig. 108. An R.F. heating installation for soldering spouts and bases to kettles.

requires skilled labour. Even so, there are many rejects if a high quality is to be maintained. The kettles become discoloured as a result of this operation and also distort, so that they are difficult to chromium plate.

Using R.F. induction heating as shown in Figure 108, the operation becomes automatic and unskilled labour is used. There are negligible rejects and a high rate of production is obtained.

The 5 kW R.F. induction heater shown in Figure 109 replaced many skilled men. In the manufacture of thermostats the assembling and soldering of the caps, nipples and tubes was a tedious business. It was difficult to maintain a sufficiently high output so that the production in the rest of the factory was delayed. The process now employs only four girls who assemble the component (Figure 110) into the jig shown in Figure 111. This is a simple operation. Completed assemblies are shown in Figure 112.

In a factory devoted to the production of gas meters, better quality and higher production has been obtained by using induction heating and unskilled labour for the soldering operations. Production line technique, as illustrated in Figures 113, 114 and 115, becomes possible. The general view in Figure 113 shows 8 work stations and a conveyor for the distribution of the component parts. Seven of the stations use 1 kW R.F. induction heaters and one station is fed from a 7½ kW R.F. generator. This station, seen in the foreground to the right of the conveyor, is illustrated in greater detail in Figure 114. The sub-assemblies are placed in jigs on the handling mechanism. They are soldered and cooled whilst moving toward the main conveyor where they are automatically off-loaded. One sub-assembly is completed every 10 seconds.

One of the 1 kW stations, which has a turntable fixture, is shown in Figure 115. The operator is seen preparing an assembly which she then places in a jig on the turntable. Thereafter, soldering, cooling, and off-loading, are automatic. One assembly is completed every 7 seconds.

9.4 WELDING

One of the oldest methods of joining like metals together is by direct welding or fusion of the parts, but it was not until well into the present century that the value of welding as an aid to greater productivity was fully appreciated.

Welding processes may be divided into two main groups:
a. direct welding, and b. indirect fusion welding.

Fig. 109. Thermostat manufacture. R.F. heating helps a difficult soldering assembly.

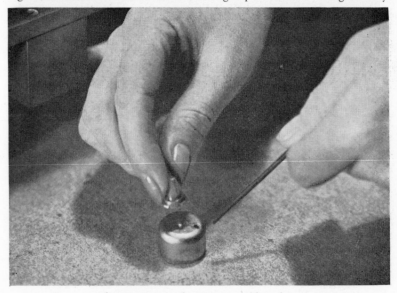

Fig. 110. Thermostat manufacture – assembling the component.

Fig. 111. Thermostat manufacture–components assembled in the work station jig.

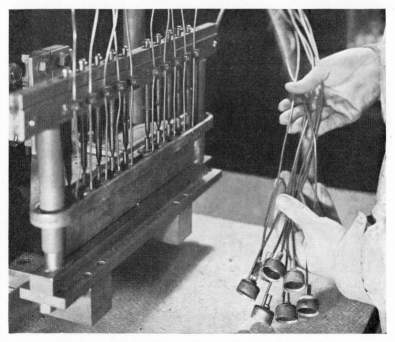

Fig. 112. Thermostat manufacture–the finished assembly.

When direct welding by forge methods, the parts are heated in a forge or furnace to a temperature a little below the melting point. The surfaces to be joined are then placed in contact with one another, to be hammered, rolled or pressed together. Very considerable skill is needed to form a satisfactory welded joint capable of withstanding repeated mechanical stress.

Fig. 113. Gas meter manufacture. General view of an R.F. heating installation for soldering and handling the component parts.

In the fusion method the parts to be welded are shaped or bevelled and metal from the electrode, in electric arc-welding, or the filler rod in gas-flame welding, is fused into the joint until it is filled.

Direct welding is frequently more satisfactory than fusion welding and an alternative and easier means of heating the parts is to pass an electric current through the joint after the parts have been properly shaped and pressed together. As the electrical resistance of the contact formed by the joint is higher than that of the surrounding metal most of the heat is generated in those surfaces which are to be joined. When they have reached a suitable temperature, additional pressure is applied to the parts to force them into intimate contact and so complete the weld.

With induction heating however, the operation becomes easier still. It is more quickly carried out, the heating is more localised, and the power consumption is lower. The weld itself is better and cleaner because oxidation is almost absent, while accurate preparation of the surfaces is unnecessary because electrical contact between them is not needed for the heating process. The mechanical pressure system is independent of the heating process so that the welding pressure may be higher to permit the use of a lower temperature for welding, and consequently there will be less deformation of the parts due to stray heating.

Fig. 114. Gas meter manufacture. View of one of the work station fixtures and an assembly conveyor.

9.4 1 WELDING APPLICATIONS

The ends of tubes are butt-welded together in a very simple machine in which the tubes are separately gripped and held in line with one another. The ends of the tubes are brought together inside a cylindrical inductor in which they are heated to welding temperature and then pressed together to form the weld.

A machine for welding the longitudinal seams of tubes from strip is illustrated in Figure 116.

The flat strip is bent by rollers to form a tube with a small gap between the edges. The formed strip with gap uppermost is passed under an iron-cored inductor when the edges are heated to welding temperature. The gap is then closed by another pair of rollers which force the edges together to complete the weld. The tube passes through a water trough for cooling and is then cut into lengths by flying shears. The position of the inductor can be adjusted to control the heating to cause the bead of welded metal to be either on the outside of the tube such as is required for smooth bore electrical conduit, or on the inside when a smooth exterior is required, such as for tubes used in the construction of modern steel furniture.

Tubes of all diameters larger than about $\frac{3}{8}$ in. can be produced from strips of low carbon steel, using a frequency of 10,000 c.p.s., at the rates given in the following table.

TABLE 8. Seam welding—rate of production.

Tube wall	Speed	kW	Tube wall	Speed	kW
.030 in.	80 ft./min.	100	.065 in.	80 ft./min.	170
	200 ft./min.	240		150 ft./min.	250
.045 in.	80 ft./min.	115	.095 in.	80 ft./min.	205
	200 ft./min.	250		120 ft./min.	250
.052 in.	80 ft./min.	140			
	175 ft./min.	250			

Radio frequency can be used for a similar process in the manufacture of tubes of aluminium and other non-ferrous metals.

9.4 2 HEATING FOR REPAIRS BY WELDING

The ease with which heat can be concentrated in a relatively small area enables induction heating to become a useful adjunct in the repair of large articles by welding. For example, the area around blow holes in large castings can be pre-heated to enable them to be filled in with weld metal. Where induction heating equipment is available it is a relatively easy matter to make a special inductor to suit the particular job.

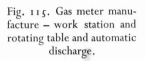

Fig. 115. Gas meter manufacture – work station and rotating table and automatic discharge.

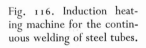

Fig. 116. Induction heating machine for the continuous welding of steel tubes.

Miscellaneous applications

10.1 GENERAL

There are many interesting specialised applications of induction heating, but those selected are indicative of the many ways in which this unique method of heating can be helpful.

10.2 FUSION AND HOT PRESSING OF METAL POWDERS

When powders of metal oxides are reduced, mixed and then sintered, the resultant structure is similar to that which would be formed by normal melting procedure. The mass may be hot pressed into forms or moulds.

Tungsten carbide powders may, for instance, be manufactured by this technique into cutting tools and dies. The induction method of heating is the most practicable one in this branch of powder metallurgy. The technique is to use induction heating as an indirect source of heat. The powder is placed in a graphite mould which is heated by induction, pressure being applied to it whilst heating. An installation shown in Figure 117 is typical. It comprises furnace emplacements, any one of which can be connected to the H.F. generator. Each furnace is mounted on a removable stillage and spare bodies of different sizes can replace those in use. Thus a range of furnaces can be available for different sizes of pressing. Pressure is applied to a furnace by the hydraulic pressure unit which moves along the gantry.

An alternative arrangement, in which the press is fixed and the furnaces are mounted on wheels, is shown in Figure 118. These are available for heating moulds for the manufacture of die rings ranging from 5 in. to 22 in. diameter. The process time is approximately one hour for each ring, but several small parts may be produced in one mould in only a few minutes.

10.3 VACUUM APPLICATION

Heating in vacuo by induction methods offers an entirely new approach to many industrial heating applications. Metals of very high purity can be melted and cast in vacuo and induction heating methods are used for the removal of dissolved gases from metals and for the analysis of those gases. It is well established as a means of heating radio valve parts and other electronic components for the purpose of drawing off occluded gases whilst the components are being evacuated, but apart from this major application, induction heating in vacuo is almost entirely confined to metallurgical research. The high-temperature heating of metals in vacuo is of growing importance however, and induction heating is almost the only practical method of accomplishing this.

10.3 1 GAS DETERMINATION IN METALS
The principle of the vacuum fusion method for the determination of oxygen, hydrogen and nitrogen in metals is to melt the metal sample in a graphite crucible in an evacuated system, and then to remove and collect the gases which are given off.

The only practicable method of melting the metal sample is by induction heating. High frequency or radio frequency power may be used.

Figure 119 illustrates equipment designed for this purpose. The inductor coil surrounding the crucible is fed from a motor generator. This coil is rated at 2 to 5 kW depending on requirements. The mouth of the crucible is closed by a graphite ball on a soft iron

Fig. 117. An installation for the high frequency fusion and hot pressing of hard metals. The pressure unit moves along the overhead gantry.

133

handle. An electro-magnet outside the vacuum chamber moves the handle to raise the ball.

In operation, the empty crucible is heated to a temperature of approximately 2,500°C and maintained at that temperature for about three hours to drive off all gases from the graphite. During this time the gases are pumped to waste. The temperature is then reduced to about 1,600°C for steel, or a lower temperature for other metals. The ball is raised to allow the metal sample to fall into the crucible in which it is melted and the gases released from it are drawn off to be collected and analysed. The method enables a skilled operator to analyse with great accuracy some 25 samples per 8 hour day.

10.4 DETERMINATION OF CARBON AND SULPHUR IN STEEL

The equipment shown in Figure 120 uses induction heating. An electrically conducting crucible is heated in a gas-tight envelope to a temperature of 1,600/1,700°C in less than a minute. The sample is placed in the crucible and a stream of oxygen is passed through the enclosure. Carbon and sulphur from the steel combine with the oxygen and the products of combustion are conveyed by external piping to the determinator units.

The power input is 500 watts at a frequency of approximately 10 mc/s.

10.5 FUSION OF GLASS

The welding of glass to metal and the jointing of glass components to one another by fusion are operations which call for the utmost skill. Even so, some glasses are particularly intractable.

Induction heating can be applied to both these operations and satisfactory results are obtainable *with unskilled labour*.

An excitron valve in course of manufacture is shown in Figure 121. The glass–of a particularly intractable quality–is welded to the metal bases with the utmost of ease. The inductor, which is fed from an R.F. generator, is controlled by a process timer; all the operator is called upon to do is to locate the parts on the work table, initiate the heating cycle, and remove the assembly when the process is completed.

An interesting technique which is growing in popularity is fusing together the two ends of glass components by placing a carbon ring over them and heating the ring inductively. The ring is uniformly heated, and consistently perfect joints are produced with

Fig. 118. Hot pressing of hard metals. The H.F. furnace units are mobile and pass under the stationary press.

Fig. 119. H.F. induction heating apparatus for determination of gaseous constituents in metals.

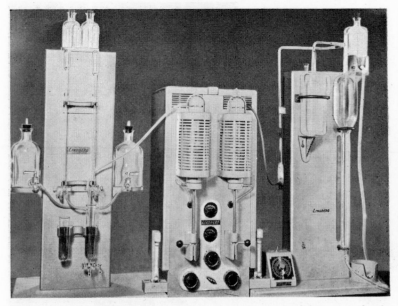

Fig. 120. Apparatus for the determination of carbon and sulphur in steel. The crucible which contains the sample is heated by R.F. induction.

unskilled labour. There are no impurities to contaminate the work such as occur when gas flames are used.

10.6 HEATING IN THE LABORATORY

An induction heater can be controlled so accurately that it can be used for research upon the effect of temperature on the structure of metals and for other similar problems.

An example of the scientific value of induction heating is shown in Figure 122, illustrating the heating of platinum to a high temperature which is maintained with such accuracy that the light emitted is used as a photometric standard.

A further example of the use of induction heating in the laboratory is the progressive heating of silicon crystals in vacuo in order to refine them. Such high-purity metals are required for the manufacture of components for modern electronic apparatus.

10.7 UNDERGROUND MINING

The cavities out of which the ore, coal, or other minerals have been taken are filled in with debris which has accumulated on the surface. In the pneumatic conveyor system the steel pipes which convey the

Fig. 121. Welding glass to metal by R.F. induction heating.

Fig. 122. R.F. heating in the research laboratory.

Fig. 123. Typical inductors for heating chemical autoclaves by normal frequency.

Fig. 124. Plant used in production of polyester resins.

crushed material from the surface to the underground workings have to withstand arduous service conditions. They require to be hardened to resist abrasion, but at the same time must also be capable of enduring considerable mechanical stress.

Pipes which have been completely hardened would have maximum wearing qualities, but would not be able to resist constant transport and handling without breaking. To overcome this the pipes are hardened in bands to give alternately hard and tough sections. The tough bands give flexibility between the hardened zones, and the resultant product therefore possesses a high degree of resistance to mechanical shock, and experience has proved that they are highly resistant to abrasion and have a long, useful life. Induction heating is the preferred method of hardening.

The operation is carried out step by step—whilst one section is being quenched the next section is being heated. This is repeated until the whole length of the pipe has been treated. The width of the hardened band is about three times that of the untreated section. For example, a pipe 6 in. in diameter would have hard bands about 1 in. wide. This size of pipe is dealt with on a 150/200 kW 10 kc motor generator plant.

10.8 INDUCTION HEATING FOR CHEMICAL AND PROCESS PLANT

The customary method of heating steel autoclaves and other containers for chemical processes is by the absorption of heat from an external source, such as a steam jacket, gas burners or electric resistance heating elements.

A convenient way, however, of raising the temperature of the vessel and its contents as rapidly as possible, without a high temperature heating source, is to use normal frequency induction heating. When an alternating current of electricity is passed through a multi-turn coil, fitted co-axially with the vessel, the wall of the vessel acts as a short circuited secondary of a transformer, and it becomes heated—much quicker than by radiation or other means of heating.

Other advantages are:

1. The ability to heat, if required, the wall of the vessel to a temperature approaching that of its magnetic change point.

2. Automatic control of temperature. Standard temperature control equipment can be utilised to

a. hold the temperature of the liquid within close limits.

b. ensure that the temperature of the skin of the vessel shall not exceed a specified critical temperature.

3. Automatic time/process control. High rates of power input are often required for heating up, and much lower powers for processing. Automatic time/process devices can be employed so that when the operating conditions have been determined experimentally, process work can be repeated with precision, using unskilled labour.

Typical normal frequency induction heating coils are illustrated in Figure 123. The internal diameter of the coil is larger than the outside diameter of the vessel to be heated, the intervening space being filled with a high-temperature lagging. The coil winding is suitably insulated for high-temperature working. A number of tapping points can be provided to vary the input of power according to conditions.

When selecting the dimensions of the vessel the height should be preferably about one and a half times the diameter or a little more. Better power factors are obtainable and the cost of the coil for a vessel of a given capacity and power input will be low in value. Units below 15 kW are generally single phase, but three-phase operation does not present difficulty. Capacitors can be used to improve the power factor.

In the field of synthetic resin manufacture induction heating enables the product under process to be heated rapidly to the temperature required, with the avoidance of hot spots or local overheating. The temperature may be held within close limits for a specified period and the rate of cooling may be controlled.

A heating vessel of 2 tons working capacity, used in the production of polyester resins, is shown in the foreground of Figure 124. An inductor coil divided into three sections for three-phase operation from the supply mains surrounds the vessel, and an exterior perforated steel cylindrical cover, approximately 72 in. in diameter, encloses the whole.

PART THREE

PART THREE

II

Dielectric heating

11.1 INTRODUCTION

Dielectric heating has been known in the past by such names as 'industrial diathermy', 'capacity current heating', 'short wave heating', 'electrostatic heating', and 'radionic heating'. The standard and accepted term for this method of heating is now 'dielectric heating'.

It was explained in the introduction that when an electrical non-conducting material is placed as shown in Figure 125 between two metal plates called electrodes, thus forming a 'dielectric', and an alternating voltage is applied across them, the material undergoes molecular disturbance, as a result of which it is heated.

There is thus no external heat source and no heat transfer by conduction, convection or radiation as in other forms of heating; dielectric heating does not heat from the outside surfaces to the inside, nor does it 'heat from the inside out'; the heat is generated within the material itself and

1. A homogeneous body of uniform section is raised in temperature uniformly throughout its mass. Uniform heating is of particular importance since no time is lost in conducting heat from the surfaces to the centre of a bulky load of low heat conducting properties.

2. The rate of heating is usually many times faster than by conventional heat transfer methods.

3. Overheating or burning the surface of temperature-sensitive materials is minimised, if not eliminated, because there is no external source of heat.

4. High thermal efficiency.

Electrical non-conducting materials–which are also poor conductors of heat–require heating for most process work to temperatures only of the order of 100°C to 120°C.

For this purpose dielectric heating can be more efficient than all other methods of heating. No idle parts are heated; and heat is generated only where it is wanted. Loss of heat by convection, conduction or radiation is limited to the surfaces of the work, and because the temperature rise is usually small in most dielectric heating applications, the loss is negligible.

5. The quantity of heat generated in the work is usually predictable and can be under positive time and power-input control.

6. Production may be started up quickly after a period of rest and during shut-down periods current is not used.

7. Vastly increased productivity is obtainable with less labour (entirely unskilled), fewer machines, and reduced floor space.

8. Flexibility of layout makes it possible to plan the factory to the best advantage. Dielectric heating may be placed in the direct line of production in the woodworking industries for example, without the risk of fire or other hazard; or the equipment may be portable and taken to the job. This eliminates the expense of handling when the work is large and cumbersome.

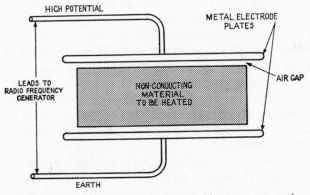

Fig. 125. Basic diagram of the process of heating non-metals by radio frequency electricity.

11.2 TECHNICAL CONSIDERATIONS

Non-metallic materials are generally poor conductors of heat. For this reason materials which can be heated by dielectric means are fundamentally difficult to heat by conventional methods. Hence, dielectric heating is a method for heating materials which are themselves not readily heated by other means.

The degree of heat which dielectric heating can generate in such materials is governed substantially by their dielectric properties and not by thermal constants. Some materials react more favourably to dielectric heating than others. It is essential, therefore, when contemplating the use of dielectric heating to have some knowledge of the dielectric properties of the materials involved and to appreciate broadly the basic difference between dielectric heating and other forms of heating.

144

The amount of heat generated in the dielectric is determined by the frequency and the square of the voltage which is applied, the dimensions of the object and a physical property of the material, termed 'loss factor'. Frequencies of some millions of cycles per second are involved and voltages up to 15,000 may be necessary for most industrial heating applications.

'Loss factor', is a convenient way of expressing the term K cos Ø in which

K = dielectric constant, a measure of a property of the material to retain energy due to movement of molecular structure.
Cos Ø = dielectric power factor of the load, that is, the ratio of the power (measured in watts) to the product (measured in volt-amperes) of the voltage and the current. This is a characteristic property of the material.

'Loss factor' is therefore a property of the material and a measure of the ease with which it can be heated by dielectric means. Like the property of thermal conductivity, it varies considerably for different substances. Under identical electric conditions of voltage and frequency, dielectric substances will each heat up at a rate dependent upon its 'loss factor', its specific heat, thermal conductivity and density.

One of the simplest applications of dielectric heating is the heating of a homogeneous body, but the behaviour of a non-homogeneous body, which comprises a mixture of two or more constituents is more complex. When such a body is placed in an electric field each constituent will heat up uniformly but each at a rate determined by its own 'loss factor', thermal properties, and density.

Should the body be a well balanced and uniform mixture any uneven generation of heat will be quickly equalised by heat conduction between adjacent particles. In a bad mixture, however, the uneven dispersion of the constituents may result in 'hot spots' and other indications of extensive temperature differences which take time to even out.

Dielectric heating is essentially a low temperature operation, and should the nature of the mixture be such that a zone of high temperature is generated at the surface of the material, sparking may occur between the electrode and the surface of the work.

Burning of the surface ensues, and a change of physical constants in the affected area may prevent effective heating in other parts.

Also release of vapours or fumes during the heating period can

K   145

cause sparking if they are not removed. Condensation of vapours on the surface of the electrodes can cause similar trouble.

Dielectric heating should not, therefore, be applied indiscriminately to the heating of mixtures. When the application is appropriate, however, considerable benefit can accrue. For example, in the woodworking industry, great use is made of the differing reactions of wood and thermo-setting glues, and in many moisture removing applications the selective heating effect enables fine control to be kept over moisture content.

11.3 SOURCE OF ELECTRICAL ENERGY

It has already been explained in the introduction that suitable apparatus must be used to raise the frequency of the commercial mains supply to a frequency of some millions of cycles per second which is necessary to make dielectric heating of industrial value.

The electronic valve provides a means of obtaining these very high frequencies and the following table gives a guide to the power, frequency and major applications for which electronic generators have been developed.

TABLE 9. Dielectric heating: applications data

R.F. Power	Frequency	Typical application
Up to 1 kW	20–100 Mc/s	Thermo-plastic welding
2 to 30 kW	10–40 Mc/s	Plastic pre-heating
		Wood glueing
Above 30 kW	2–10 Mc/s	Plywood moulding

Note: 1 Mc = 1,000,000 cycles

Voltages ranging from 2,000 up to 15,000 may be necessary, depending upon the application.

Standard generator units are available giving a few hundred watts up to 100 kW of R.F. output.

The component parts of an R.F. generator for dielectric heating are shown diagrammatically in Figure 126. The arrangement is similar to that of an R.F. generator for induction heating. It is seldom, however, that variables such as the shape, size, and physical constants of the work and the electrode assembly can be chosen to obtain the optimum performance of a given generator, and changes may occur in the electrical characteristics of the material during the heating process. Therefore, it is advantageous sometimes to introduce a matching unit, or transformer, as shown in the diagram, between the generator and the load.

11.4 MAINTENANCE

Maintenance of dielectric heating equipment is similar to that out-lined for R.F. Induction Heating generators (see Chapter 2).

When generating frequencies of some millions of cycles per sec-ond, the presence of dust and surface contamination on the insula-tion in the oscillator section may give rise to surface leakages and impair the efficiency of the generator. Valve generators, when used for dielectric heating purposes, should receive regular routine cleaning.

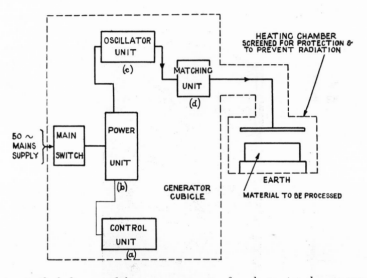

Fig. 126. Block diagram of the component parts of an electronic valve generator for dielectric heating.

11.5 LAYOUT

The layout of dielectric heating equipment is very flexible and the heating process may be planned either in, or adjacent to the main line of factory production. This is extremely beneficial in factories where the hazard of fire is high, and conventional types of furnaces would not be permitted.

The heating electrodes may be an integral part of the generator, or they may be linked by cable to the generator located in some convenient position remote from the actual process work. No safety protection is required other than that afforded by the cubicle and work station enclosure.

High-voltage radio frequency power is not lethal like normal frequency power at the same voltage but it can cause skin burning should live or other exposed metal parts be touched. Questions have often been raised regarding the risk of biological hazard to the operator. The frequencies at present used for industrial heating purposes are, however, not high enough to cause deterioration of human tissue.

The only danger, therefore, is that of skin burning, and the safety of the operator is ensured by screening all vulnerable points in the valve generator, with earthed metallic enclosures.

Fig. 127. Typical R.F. generator.

In the majority of applications the work stations also are similarly enclosed, either completely or partially. The enclosures may be of wire mesh construction, and where access is required for loading and unloading purposes they are hinged and interlocked so that all live parts are dead when the enclosure is opened.

For photographic purposes the screens have been removed from some of the work stations illustrated but in others the enclosure arrangements are shown. In some applications, such as for example, the welding of thermo-plastic materials in the production of garments and fancy goods, the operator feeds the material on to, and positions it by hand over the live electrode. It is not practicable to place a metallic enclosure round the operator's work table, but complete protection is ensured by using safety switches to prevent the power from being applied until the material is in contact with the electrodes and the welding pressure has been established.

11.7 RADIO FREQUENCY INTERFERENCE WITH TELEVISION AND OTHER RADIO SERVICES

The frequency most suitable for many dielectric heating applications falls very close to the television wave band. Complete screening of all dielectric heating equipment is, therefore, recommended. In most applications the metallic screening necessary for the safety of the operators is sufficient to minimise interference, to an acceptable degree, and to conform to H.M. Post Office regulations.

11.8 CONTROL OF DIELECTRIC HEATING

It is customary for all dielectric heating operations to be controlled by a process timer.

Initial trials are carried out upon the material to be processed and when the required heating results are obtained the time interval is checked accurately and the process timer set accordingly.

This is reset whenever there is a change of product; but as most dielectric heating installations are used on repetition production work–in which sphere the full benefit of dielectric methods is obtained–changes in the heating cycle are infrequent.

Should the temperature of the work be required during the heating cycle for experimental or other purposes, a thermocouple or other temperature responsive device may be used, but as the presence of the measuring device may distort the electric field or alter the rate of heat generation in the immediate vicinity, a false reading may be obtained. It is customary, therefore, to insert the couple or other measuring device only when the current is switched off.

11.9 LOAD FACTOR

More than one work station, press, or heating process unit may be operated from a single generator. When suitable output switches and interlocking devices are fitted, the process timer will cut off the R.F. power to the first station at the end of the heating cycle and in a few seconds switch power on to No. 2 station, and so on. A typical generator is shown in Figure 127. It is of 7 kW R.F. output and at a frequency of 10 Mc/s. The three-way co-axial switch shown in the illustration enables three work stations to be fed consecutively with R.F. power. When the factory layout and production methods are suitably planned R.F. generators may operate at almost 100 per cent load factor.

Dielectric heating
for plastics

12.1 GENERAL

Dielectric heating has played a very important part in the phenomenal growth of the plastics industries.

Synthetic organic compounds have become new materials of construction, rivalling the metals in strength, whilst retaining the characteristic non-metallic properties of lightness and resistance to corrosion by water. These organic compounds are bad conductors of heat, but possess excellent properties for dielectric heating. It is difficult to heat them by conventional heat transfer methods, but they react readily to dielectric methods of heating.

Two classes of compounds predominate–thermo-setting and thermo-plastic. Both classes require heat processing in some stage of manufacture.

Urea formaldehyde and phenol formaldehyde are examples of the thermo-setting class. As the name implies they are hardened by heat. The reaction is a chemical one and irreversible; that is, when the chemical change in the substance is brought about its original state cannot be regained.

Thermo-plastic resins, which include cellulose acetates and nitrates, and the nylon group, soften with heat–no chemical change takes place in the material, unless it is overheated when decomposition takes place–and they regain their original state upon cooling.

12.2 THERMO-SETTING PLASTIC MOULDING POWDERS

The first stage in the cycle of operations for the production of plastic mouldings is the heating of the plastic material to its softening point. When this is done by heat conduction from the moulds the initial softening stage is the limiting factor in the production rate of the press. As all moulding powders are poor conductors of heat the comparatively long time taken in this initial stage means that production rates can be increased only by installing more presses.

In the early development of moulded plastic components, and during the last war when the need for output was paramount, it was

Fig. 128. A 1,600-ton press installation for moulding console type television cabinets. The 32 lb. load of moulding material has been preheated to 70 °C in the 6 kW dielectric heater alongside.

found that production rates could be substantially increased when the moulding powder, in the form of pellets or preforms, was preheated before press moulding.

Infra-red heating and dielectric heating were used for the purpose, and today dielectric preheating of the preforms for large mouldings has become standard practice. Without dielectric heating the production of many large mouldings as shown in Figure 128 would be found to be quite impracticable.

Uniform through heating of the moulding powder—unobtainable by most other methods of heating—softens it to the consistency of putty and moulding pressures may be reduced by one third to one half; there is less tool wear and an improvement in the final surface finish of the moulding. At a conservative estimate tool life is doubled, and as the tool is a costly item of press plant the saving in tool costs alone quickly repays the capital outlay on the dielectric heating installation. The powder may be preheated to a temperature very close to the curing point; the time required for curing in the mould is, therefore, greatly shortened and the output of the press correspondingly increased.

Fig. 129. Preheating before press moulding. A typical R.F. preheater 2 kW output. One of 20 in a large press shop.

Fig. 130. R.F. generator and heating chamber. The lid of the cabinet is shown in the open position for loading and unloading.

Fig. 131. Fabricating a plastic garment – welding the hems.

Taking all these factors into consideration, the introduction of dielectric preheating can increase the productive capacity of the press by 200 per cent to 300 per cent.

Existing presses may, therefore, be used for larger work, or if a new press is contemplated then a smaller unit at a lower price would suffice.

Figure 129 shows part of an installation of 20 preheater units each unit serving one press. Preheating units are available in sizes ranging from about 350 watts up to 10 kW or more, but units of 1, 2, or 3 kW of radio frequency output are the sizes most frequently installed.

The heating chamber may be designed as a separate unit or it may be built integral with the R.F. generator (Figure 130). Sometimes the cubicle is mounted on castors to facilitate movement about the presses.

The electrodes comprise two flat plates, one usually at earth potential and the other at high voltage. Either electrode may be the higher voltage member depending upon the disposition of the oscillator within the unit, but interlocking switches are provided so that the supply of radio frequency energy to the electrodes is

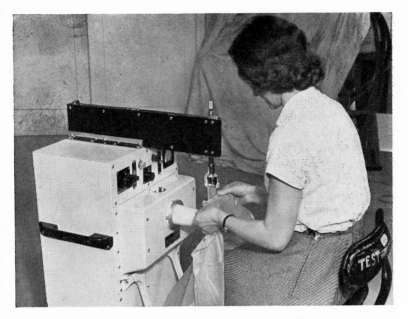

Fig. 132. Fabricating a plastic garment – welding the collar of a raincoat.

automatically disconnected when the cabinet lid or hood is opened for loading and unloading purposes.

As a rough guide it may be taken that about ¾ lb. of moulding powder can be preheated in one minute for each kilowatt of R.F. power taken from the generator.

Heating is controlled by a process timer which may be set to a predetermined time cycle.

12.3 THERMO-PLASTICS

12.3 1 WELDING AND FUSING

An important and extensive application of dielectric heating in the plastic industry is the welding of thin sheets of thermo-plastic materials for the fabrication of commonly used articles such as raincoats, plastic covers, handbags, tobacco cases, note-cases, and packaging materials for industrial purposes. Dielectric heating methods have given such remarkably good results that they have largely replaced other techniques in many factories.

Sheets of polyvinyl chloride from which such commodities are made are only a few thousandths of an inch thick and when heated to fusion point under pressure two or more thicknesses are fused and welded together to form seams, to secure button pads, and to eliminate stitching which weakens the joint.

Thermo-plastic materials, of which P.V.C. is an example, are extremely temperature sensitive and the conventional method of clamping the sheets between heated dies introduces so many uncontrollable variables that the outer surfaces can become hotter and, therefore, more plastic than the inner layers. This results in weak, uneven joints, the sheets become deformed and if the temperature exceeds a narrow critical value the material will decompose. Dielectric heating on the other hand, is stable and controllable and the rise of temperature up to the fusion point of the P.V.C. is very rapid. Heat is generated through the thickness of the assembly, but as the outside surfaces are gripped by relatively cold metal electrodes the highest temperature is reached at the centre where the fusion is required. The other surfaces remain comparatively unaffected by heat and the risk of over-heating common to all heat conduction methods of heating is greatly minimised.

12.3 2 PLASTIC GARMENT MANUFACTURE

The adaptability of dielectric heating methods to a new and thriving industry is clearly shown in Figures 131 to 133 which illustrate stages in the manufacture of a plastic raincoat. Figure 131 shows an operator welding the hem of a plastic raincoat by means of a series of overlapping bar welds. The machine is fitted with a table bracket which enables the pattern to be laid out flat when welding. The welding cycle is approximately 1 second.

A similar R.F. work station, used for working round the collar of the coat is shown in Figure 132.

Most of the welding of P.V.C. raincoats is usually done by a series of overlapping, straight, curved, or bar welds. There are, however, certain operations, such as patch pockets, collars, buttonhole facings, which require the use of special electrode die forms. Figure 133 shows a typical die of this type to produce a reinforcement patch under the sleeve of the coat.

12.3 3 DIELECTRIC HEATING AND FANCY GOODS MANUFACTURE

In the manufacture of such articles as wallets, note-cases and handbags in P.V.C. material, the patterns are first cut out and preliminary welding is carried out on small parts such as fastening tabs and loops, stamp and ticket pockets. The finished patterns are then placed in a sliding loading frame and the article completed on a welding unit

Fig. 133. Fabricating a plastic garment – illustration of a shaped electrode to produce a reinforcement patch under the sleeve of a coat.

Fig. 134. Fancy goods manufacture. Pattern cutting knives, component parts and the loading frame for holding the parts for final welding to produce the wallet shown in the foreground.

Fig. 135. Seam welding P.V.C. material by radio frequency.

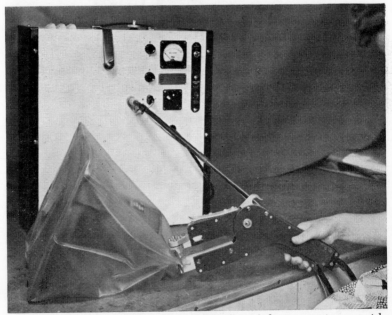

Fig. 136. Hand application for seam welding thermo-plastic wrapping materials.

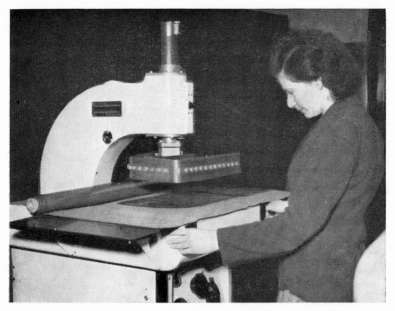

Fig. 137. A typical R.F. unit 6 kW output for profile welding. Electrode die forms are made in special shapes to suit the application. The operator is seen welding a transparent vinyl backlight to the hood material of a motor car.

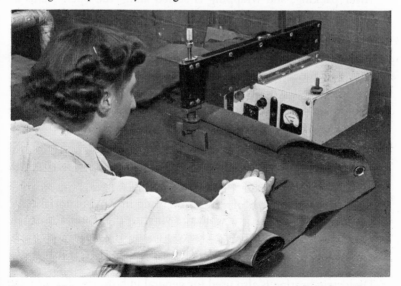

Fig. 138. Using a 300 watt R.F. generator to repair worn P.V.C. protective clothing. The patching is water and oil proof.

similar to that illustrated in Figure 131. Approximately 1 kW is required for the profile weld of a wallet such as the one illustrated in Figure 134.

12.3 4 DIELECTRIC HEATING FOR THE CINEMA

Cinema screens of P.V.C. material may be seam welded by radio frequency.

Figure 135 shows a $\frac{3}{4}$ kW bar welder making the seams of a large screen. The welder itself is mounted on rails which run alongside the bench on which the material is laid out. The operator sits at the side of the machine which she controls by a foot-operated pedal.

12.3 5 DIELECTRIC HEATING IN THE PACKAGING INDUSTRY

The immense growth of thermo-plastic materials for use as protective wrappings for food-stuffs and textiles and for coverings to exclude moisture from machine parts, and to prevent micro-biological attack of other commodities, is proving a fertile and profitable field for dielectric heating methods.

Patterns are cut out and seam welded by placing between pairs of straight electrodes. Intricate shapes or numbers of seals may be welded at one setting by using special electrode die forms.

After packing, the wrapping is sealed along the open seams by means of a portable welding machine and a typical applicator for the purpose (Figure 136) shows an R.F. generator feeding a plier type hand applicator by means of a co-axial feeder. Low voltage switching arrangements are incorporated in the handle, so that the applicator conforms to H.M. safety regulations for factories. The generator provides approximately $\frac{1}{4}$ kW at 37 Mc/s.

Equipment of this type is widely used in the packaging of machine parts and for applications in other plastic welding fields such as spot welding and fast overlapping short bar welds.

12.3 6 DIELECTRIC HEATING IN THE MOTOR CAR INDUSTRY

Recent developments in P.V.C. compounds have now enabled hoods and screens of motor cars to be made in vinyl materials, and dielectric heating is used to weld the vinyl to the material forming the hood of a soft-topped car; Figure 137 illustrates the welding of a transparent vinyl back light to the hood material. The material itself is a heavy canvas with a P.V.C.-coated surface.

Dielectric heating is also used for general upholstery of motor-car interiors, such as the bonding of door pads.

Fig. 139. Laundry marking machine and a portable R.F. generator of 100 watts output. Delicate fabrics may be marked without detriment to the tissue.

Fig. 140. Welding rubber fingers to a P.V.C. coated canvas belt of a potato harvesting machine.

Fig. 141. Dielectric heater for welding a P.V.C. coil used in television equipment.

Waterproof aprons used as protective garments become cut and torn and quickly lose their value. Instead of discarding them, cuts and tears can be repaired very rapidly by welding. A work station fitted with electrodes for this work is shown in Figure 138. Similar repair work in the many industries in which protective clothing is necessary should prove beneficial.

12.3 7 PLASTIC ADHESION BETWEEN FABRICS

Ordinary woven fabrics may be joined together by introducing a thin strip of plastic sheet between them.

When passed between the electrodes of a dielectric welding machine the plastic heats up and softens but the fabric remains unheated. Consolidating rolls force the soft plastic into the fabric, and upon cooling, excellent adhesion is obtained.

Use is also made of plastic adhesion to ordinary woven fabric in the laundry and Figure 139 illustrates a machine for fusing serial markings to articles to be laundered. A plastic tape with markings on the under side is interposed between the article and the top electrode. Depression of the foot-operated pedal closes the circuit; the tape becomes hot and softens, and final pressure on the pedal registers the serial mark or number on the fabric. The marking is permanent for all ordinary purposes but should it be necessary to remove it the marking may be peeled off like Sellotape.

Dielectric heating has proved more satisfactory than hot ironing or other heat conduction methods for this application because the heat is generated only in the plastic adhesive, the woven fabric surfaces remaining comparatively cool.

Thermo-plastic materials are used in an increasing number of industries, and many specialised industrial applications of plastic welding have been developed. Two examples are illustrated. Figure 140 shows rubber fingers being welded to a heavy P.V.C. coated canvas belt, used on a potato harvesting machine. The fingers are welded on this, six at a time, one die being loaded whilst the other is in operation. The second example (Figure 141) shows a welded P.V.C. coil for use in television apparatus.

The examples are taken from two different types of industry, but in most industries the commercial use of new synthetic materials may become more extensive when dielectric heating methods are used.

Dielectric heating
in the woodworking industries

13.1 GENERAL

The most important development in recent years in the wood-working industries has been the introduction of synthetic resin adhesives of the thermo-setting type for the bonding and adhesion of wood components. Three types of synthetic resins are available, namely urea and phenol formaldehyde, and melamine. In the furniture and plywood industries urea formaldehyde is mostly employed.

Synthetic resin glues are resistant to water and to micro-biological attack. Joints bonded with these synthetic compounds are at least equal to, and in many instances better than, those in which the traditional animal glue is the adhesive.

Unlike natural animal glues, which harden by cooling and by loss of moisture, hardening or curing of thermo-setting resins is an irreversible chemical reaction which proceeds at a rate largely determined by temperature. For instance, urea formaldehyde may be cured and set in three hours at a temperature of 65°F; in one hour at 80°F; in three minutes at 150°F and in one minute at 190°F. The resultant bonded joint is equally satisfactory in each case. Wood is a poor conductor of heat and if the component is thick or bulky, time is lost before conducted heat reaches the embedded joints. Consequently production rates may be increased many times by the simple expedient of heating the glue line. This may be done by the conduction of heat from an external source such as steam, hot water, electric strip or mesh heating elements or by the generation of heat in the glue line by dielectric heating methods.

Heating by radio frequency is, however, very rapid; consequently the property of quick-setting resins may be used to full advantage when the dielectric method of heating is applied. However, it may not always be desirable or necessary to take advantage of this property. For instance, no economic advantage would be gained from a substantial reduction in the glueing time if, in the line of production there are unavoidable retarding factors which would result in no overall increase in factory output.

In the woodworking industries, more than in most others, it is wise to appreciate that dielectric heating is not just another method of heating, and where existing methods are satisfactory very careful consideration must be given to all the factors involved before replacing them by dielectric heating.

On the other hand, the use of dielectric heating permits new ideas, or novel designs to be adopted, which would not otherwise be practicable; and where the components are thick and heating by conventional methods therefore slow, dielectric heating has much to offer.

What suits one factory, producing a standard article, may not suit another which has a more variable output, and although the application of dielectric heating has been in many factories the greatest factor in the battle to produce more at less cost, dielectric heating should not be adopted until all the factors involved have been investigated. Should the application be suitable then dielectric heating can prove of inestimable benefit to the industry concerned.

13.2 PLYWOOD MANUFACTURE

13.2 1 FLAT SHEETS

Old types of multi-daylight presses with 10 or 12 pairs of steam-heated platens are still in general use. One plywood assembly is heated and cured between each pair of platens, the time taken to heat and cure a $\frac{1}{2}$ in. thick assembly being 10 to 15 minutes.

Using dielectric heating methods this could be reduced to a minute or two, but as it requires some 10 to 15 minutes to assemble the next load, no productive advantage would be gained.

In the single daylight press of the type shown in Figure 142 economic factors are, however, favourable to dielectric heating. Power is consumed only during the actual heating cycle and in comparison with the multi-daylight steam-heated press, where steam is on all the time, there may be considerable saving in heating costs.

The press illustrated holds 100 3-ply assemblies each approximately $\frac{1}{2}$ in. thick. Complete through-heating to a temperature of approximately 200°F and curing of the resin glue is obtained in 20 to 30 minutes, depending upon the dryness of the wood. An output of up to 60 cubic feet of plywood per hour can be obtained when operated from a generator of 25 kW of R.F. output.

During the heating cycle a pressure of 150 to 200 lb. per sq. in. must be maintained on the stack, and to avoid the problems of designing a pressure platen which has also to serve as a high-voltage electrode, the live electrode, in the form of a thin metal sheet, is

Fig. 142. Plywood manufacture – glue setting in a single daylight press. Note the live electrode at the centre and the earth electrodes—one at the bottom and one at the top of the stack.

Fig. 143. Fabricating complex wooden shapes built up from wood laminations. Dielectric heating reduces the setting time of the glue to a few minutes.

placed in the middle of the stack, the top and bottom pressure platens of the press becoming the earth electrode.

13.2 2 CURVED LAMINATED SHAPES

Increasing use is being made of complex laminated shapes in the construction of furniture of contemporary design. Flat wood laminations, coated with synthetic adhesive, are held under pressure between wooden formers shaped to the finished product.

At ordinary workshop temperatures a curing time of 8 hours is necessary, during which time the press is immobile. When large quantities are required many presses are necessary which occupy a large floor area. However, the curing time can be greatly reduced when the assemblies are heated and this results in an increased output from the press. A smaller floor space is therefore required for a given production. Convenient methods of heating are electric resistance strip heating, and dielectric heating.

Resistance heating, which heats the assembly by conduction, cures the resin adhesive at the rate of approximately one minute per mm. of depth plus the glue setting time.

Dielectric heating, which generates heat within the assembly, can cure one pound weight of laminations in a total time of one minute for each kW of R.F. energy consumed.

Typical comparative figures are shown in the table below.

TABLE 10. Comparative data – heating and setting times

| Total thickness of laminations | Total heating and setting time in minutes | |
	Conduction heating	Dielectric heating
1 in.	20	4
$\frac{3}{8}$ in.	$5\frac{1}{2}$	$2\frac{1}{2}$
0.6 mm. veneer	1	$1\frac{1}{4}$

When the assemblies are thin the choice of dielectric or conduction methods of heating depends upon local economics, but where thick assemblies are involved there are few applications in which dielectric heating would not be outstandingly advantageous.

A single press fed from an R.F. generator is satisfactory for small outputs, but when a high rate of production is required, two or more presses fed, in sequence, from a common generator is more economical. The arrangement permits the generator to operate at a high load factor and the productive efficiency of the plant is increased.

An installation consisting of two hand-operated presses is shown in Figure 143.

Fig. 144. Manufacture of curved laminated shapes. Three press units are fed in sequence from one 8 kW R.F. generator. A high load factor is maintained and in consequence capital cost and operating costs are low.

These presses are used for the manufacture of legs and back frames of laminated chairs. The laminated assemblies, having an area of 4.59 sq. ft. and comprising 30 laminations of 1 mm. thick beech veneers, can be formed and cured in three minutes. From this one shape eight sections are cut on a finishing saw and the final product is clean and pleasing to the eye. With other methods the rate of heating through the mass would be too slow to meet production demands.

Another installation in which three power-operated presses are fed from an 8 kW R.F. generator is illustrated in Figure 144. Dressing-table ends, two at a time, are heated and set in one minute, with an R.F. input of 6 kW under the press form on the extreme right; 36 in. radius shapes, $\frac{3}{4}$ in. thick, for drawer fronts in $1\frac{1}{2}$ minutes with an input of 6 kW from the middle unit, and on the extreme right a 70 in. radius plinth is made in half-a-minute with an input of 8 kW.

Fig. 145. Block-board manufacture – dielectric heating is used to reduce the glue setting time from many hours to several minutes.

13.3 LAMINATED BOARDS

Boards comprising thin laminations of paper, fabric, or asbestos, may be treated in the same way as wood laminations.

When thin sheets coated with a thermo-setting synthetic resin are stacked to the required thickness, put under pressure, and radio frequency power applied, a uniform temperature is generated throughout the mass. The risk of overheating or burning the outside surfaces is eliminated and production rates per unit of floor space are very substantially increased.

13.4 BLOCK BOARD MANUFACTURE

Large boards may be formed from numbers of wood strips planed to uniform thickness and glued together on the edge. A veneer may be applied to the surface when the board is to be used for table tops and chair seats.

The conventional method of manufacture is to select a set of

Fig. 146. Furniture assembly – positioning the wood components of a wardrobe sub-assembly into the glueing jig. The glue joints are set in one minute when placed between the dielectric heating electrodes of the press. The protective screening has been removed for photographic purposes.

strips, which may be of varying widths and lengths, apply glue to the edge faces, place in a clamping jig and tighten the clamps to provide transverse pressure across the glue lines. After one hour the glue has set sufficiently to hold the assembly together. The assembly is then transferred to a warm room where, after a further 12 to 48 hours, depending upon the size of the board, the glue has set to maximum hardness.

This application is an excellent one for dielectric heating. After the preliminary preparation and assembly of the parts, the glue may be set to maximum hardness in 1 to 10 minutes depending upon the circumstances. The productive capacity per unit of floor space is very materially increased, and there are considerable savings in heat costs, labour, and jigging costs.

Figure 144 illustrates a fully mechanised equipment. The arrangement of electrodes is such that they are brought into intimate contact with the top and bottom surfaces of the assembly, so the R.F. voltage is applied along the glue lines. The glue heats up much more rapidly than the adjacent wood and at the end of the curing cycle the rise in temperature of the wood is very slight. Thus a large portion of the total energy used for the glueing operation has been applied to the glue. Power consumption is consequently low. Using an R.F. generator of 5 kW output, production rates up to 600 square inches of glue line, set to maximum hardness, may be obtained in one minute, the actual rate depending to some extent on the nature of the wood and the precise type of synthetic glue used.

13.5 FURNITURE ASSEMBLY

13.5 1 GLUEING OF WOOD COMPONENTS

The glueing or bonding of components is a major operation in the furniture and other wood-working trades and there are many applications in which dielectric heating could be applied very profitably.

The quickness with which synthetic resin adhesives can be hardened increases the rate of production and conserves floor space. Fewer jigs are involved and less labour is required. The heating equipment can be placed in the direct line of production, thus reducing handling to a minimum.

In the manufacture of furniture and joinery products wood assemblies may be secured entirely by glueing, and a typical installation for the glueing of assemblies is shown in Figure 146. The sub-assemblies consist mainly of end panels of a suite of bedroom furniture. The end panel has attached to it the shelf bearers, top and bottom rails and front and rear stiles.

The old method of attaching these rails to the panel was either by screwing or pinning and then placing in a hand screw press until the resin adhesive had cured. The curing time of resin adhesives depends entirely on temperature; if the workroom is at low temperature, then the curing or setting time increases. With this older method the presses occupy a great deal of floor space and the work is handled several times.

After the change-over to dielectric heating, the rate of production was increased from 100 to 450 suites per week, using the original floor space. Each suite consists of two wardrobe end panels, two tallboy end panels and two dressing-table end panels.

The plant can be operated by two unskilled workers. Process timers control the curing cycle automatically and the parts produced are uniform in quality.

The installation consists of a pneumatic press, the ends of which are open. This permits the work to be fed alternately from each end into the press, thereby maintaining an almost continuous flow of work and a high operating condition of the R.F. generator. Jigs are used to facilitate the assembly of the components. On loading a jig with the parts associated with the particular panel the whole assembly is pushed into the pneumatic press, and when pressure is applied, R.F. energy is switched on, and the glue lines of the assembly are set in one minute. The assembly is then removed from the press and immediately another is inserted from the opposite end, and the cycle of operations is repeated. The installation is fed from a 3 kW R.F. generator.

Another modern installation for the assembly of kitchen cabinets is illustrated in Figure 147. The use of dielectric heating has not only increased the rate of production and reduced the costs of manufacture, but it has also permitted the introduction of new methods of construction, resulting in a product of much cleaner appearance.

In the manufacture of flush doors, fitting the wood beading (lipping) to the sides of the doors can retard production. One method of manufacture is to place the door in cramps and allow the resin adhesive to set under shop temperature conditions. The setting time varies from two to three hours.

This can be reduced to less than one minute, when dielectric

Figure 147. Setting the glue joints of kitchen cabinet assemblies by R.F. heating. Shelf bearers, top and bottom rails and back and front stiles of an end panel are attached to the ply panel in one operation. The pneumatic press is open at each end thus allowing a shuttle operation of the work pieces and thereby maintaining a high load factor on the R.F. generator.

Fig. 148. Flush-door manufacture. Setting the glue joints occupies one minute when dielectric heating is used.

heating methods are used. A press with electrodes arranged to set the glued surface of the lippings in one operation is shown in Figure 148. R.F. power is obtained from a 6 kW generator. The doors are pushed into the electrode area, pressure is applied and the R.F. power is switched on. When the heating cycle is complete, pressure is released and the door proceeds on the conveyor to the next operation. Unnecessary handling of the doors is avoided, floor space is conserved, and labour is reduced.

13.5 2 ELECTRODES, JIGS AND FIXTURES
The successful application of dielectric heating depends largely upon the shape and the position of the electrodes, relative to the assembly, and upon the design of the jigs which locate and hold the components under pressure during heating. The position of the electrodes determines the efficiency of heating. When they are placed so that the R.F. field which is set up is substantially parallel to the glue line (longitudinal or glue line heating), selective heating of the glue takes place with only a slight rise in the temperature of the adjacent wood. When the field is at right angles to the glue line (transverse heating), selective heating does not occur and the total mass becomes through heated.

It is preferable to use the glue line method of heating wherever this is practicable, because it is much more efficient than transverse heating.

Good design of electrodes can help in the conservation of power, and well-designed jigs and fixtures can reduce assembly times and improve the productive capacity of the plant. In the furniture industry a great deal depends upon the ability of the man in charge, to adapt or construct the jigs and fixtures in order to avoid production delays when the design of the product changes. It is customary for the jigs and fixtures to be made by the user, and the equipment manufacturer often undertakes to give to customers' operators the necessary theoretical and practical instruction to enable them to deal with these day to day problems of operation.

Experimental and research work may be necessary with some applications and the well-trained theoretical and practical man on the spot, with time to study the subject and apply the results of his work, may be better able to develop his own application than the plant manufacturer whose primary concern lies in the highly technical aspect of the generation of high frequency electricity.

13.6 RESIN BONDED WOOD-CHIP BOARD

A substitute for natural timber is made by utilising the wood waste from saw mills and cuttings from the lumber industry. These are broken down to a coarse size, mixed with a synthetic resin and heated under pressure to set the resin.

A mass having a depth of 6 to 8 inches is required to produce a board $\frac{1}{2}$ in. thick. The mixture is an extremely poor conductor of heat and requires a pressing operation of long duration and slow curing when conventional heating methods are used.

The use of radio frequency shortens heating and curing times and because of the increased fluidity obtained by uniform through heating, less powerful presses may be used for the production of a board of a given size.

Another line of approach is to preheat the mass uniformly by dielectric heating before it enters the press. When this is done, ordinary conduction heating of the press plates is sufficient to maintain the temperature and plasticity of the mass during pressing and curing.

A continuous press equipment in which dielectric preheating is adopted is illustrated in Figure 149. The dielectric unit comprises heaters with a total output of 90 kW of R.F. and the sawdust and resin mixture is heated to approximately 85° to 90°C as it passes under the electrodes; sheets 4 ft. wide are produced at a rate of 2

Fig. 149. Continuous press for the production of a resin bonded chip-board. The illustration shows the mixture passing under the dielectric heating electrodes to be preheated before it enters the press.

Fig. 150. Portable applicator for tack glueing and for setting the glue in small joints.

Fig. 151. Tack glueing a plywood assembly with a hand applicator.

to 3 tons per hour. Without this rapid through heating, immediately before pressing, the process would be impracticable as both the pressure and the length of the press would have to be several times as great. Installations such as this have a vital role to play in a wide range of new processes which, without dielectric heating, might be impossible.

13.7 SPOT GLUEING

Increased production and lower costs can result when R.F. power is taken to the work instead of bringing the work up to a fixed work station and generator. Portable generators and hand applicators have been developed for tack glueing components which are being prepared for final glueing so that no jigging is necessary and for setting the glue in small joints.

Figure 150 illustrates one type of portable applicator. The live electrode is supported by two Pyrex insulators shown on the right. The rectangular electrode illustrated may be detached and a small spot electrode screwed on to one insulator in its place. The applicator is fed from a portable R.F. generator which will give up to 500 watts and when the electrode is energised, a concentrated field is produced which penetrates the wood adjacent to areas upon which the electrode is impressed.

Another small hand unit illustrated in Figure 151 is useful for tack glueing panels and veneers to a foundation structure. It is fed through a flexible co-axial cable from a portable R.F. generator giving 500 to 700 watts R.F. output.

Miscellaneous applications

14.1 DIELECTRIC HEATING IN THE FOUNDRY

14.1 1 BAKING SAND CORES

The traditional method of foundry sand-core manufacture is to bond a moist sand mixture with a vegetable binding agent. Heated in an oven, moisture is extracted and the binding agent oxidises and holds the sand particles together. The oxidation rate is slow. Consequently the process is a long one.

Towards the end of the last war, when supplies of linseed oil–the agent most frequently used–became limited and costly, synthetic resin-type binders were introduced as a substitute and a new technique of sand-core manufacture was evolved.

Using radio frequency, heat is generated rapidly and uniformly throughout the mixture, the water is quickly evaporated, and full use is made of the quick-setting properties of the resin binder.

Heating cycles of hours which are common with oil binders and conventional ovens, are reduced to minutes when resin-bonded sands are heated by dielectric methods.

Unpleasant fumes are removed, working conditions are vastly improved, and there is saving of floor space.

Because the speed of operation is high, it is possible to maintain a high production rate of mouldings and to make production changes at short notice without keeping large stocks of cores in the foundry. The number of core plates in circulation may also be reduced very considerably. Further, it is claimed by users of the new technique that the quality of the core is improved–surfaces are smoother and harder and the castings which are produced are cleaner and require less fettling. Uniform through heating eliminates cracking and distortion, and consequently core rejects are minimised.

The greatest advantage is to be gained when a long run of similar cores is possible, and for this purpose fully mechanised plants of the continuous conveyor type, as illustrated in Figure 152, have been developed.

Although cores of different sizes may be baked simultaneously on the same unit, maximum heating efficiency and quality of product is obtained when the cores are all substantially the same size and

Fig. 152. Dielectric heating in the foundry core shop. Continuous conveyor core baking equipment. Production rates 1,000 lbs. of cores per hour.

thickness. The speed of the conveyor is adjusted to suit the conditions of loading.

1 kW of R.F. generator output will bake from 30 to 60 lb. of cores per hour, depending upon circumstances. With electricity at 1d. per unit the cost of power (drawn from the mains) is approximately 6/3d. to 12/6d. per ton of cores.

14.1 2 RESIN BONDED SHELL MOULDS

Mechanisation of the foundry has resulted in an increasing application of the shell-moulding process.

In the early stages of development, resin-bonded sands were moulded under pressure and partially cured in the moulding machine. Final hardening took place at normal shop temperature, followed by assembly of the two sections of the mould by various mechanical means—i.e., clips, bent nails, or nuts and bolts. The process was slow and the method of assembly was not entirely reliable, but since shell moulding has become mechanised, and applicable, therefore, to the large production foundry, it is necessary to have better and quicker methods to harden the moulds and to assemble them.

Dielectric heating methods can be used for both purposes, with

Fig. 153. R.F. equipment for bonding shell moulds.

a reduction in the reserve stock of moulds, smaller floor space requirements, and a better and more consistent product.

Figure 153 illustrates a standard R.F. generator used for bonding
cold shells. The work station in front of the generator comprises a
pair of electrodes, and a clamping device which holds the shells
together by a number of spring-loaded 'fingers' which can be adjusted to suit shells of different contours.

One shell is treated with a resin adhesive, and the other, to which no adhesive has been applied, is closed with the treated shell, and the complete mould placed in position in the clamping device. On pulling a lever the shells are pressed together. A button is pushed; the radio-frequency field heats up the glue line only, and the adhesive is hardened completely in about 15 seconds. The electric field is switched off automatically and the lever is pushed back to release the shells which are then taken from the clamping device.

14.2 RUBBER AND DIELECTRIC HEATING

The use of dielectric heating for the vulcanising of rubber was one of the earliest industrial applications.

When latex is rendered heat sensitive by the addition of certain agents it will coagulate when heated. If a mass of treated latex is heated by conventional methods the final result tends to be hollow in the centre and more compact on the outside. Furthermore, a long time is required for the heat to penetrate into a thick mass of latex. Dielectric heating in a uniform field enables the coagulation to be uniform throughout the mass and the process can be completed rapidly.

Heat-sensitised latex can be frothed, fed into a rubber tray and passed progressively between the electrodes of a dielectric heater. Heating is uniform and the mass can be gelled without impairing the froth structure. The product is then vulcanised to result in sponge rubber.

Dielectric heating methods are also very suitable for the continuous vulcanising of rubber on electric cables, and when rubber is preheated by these methods before passing on to the moulding press, curing times are reduced, the rate of production is increased, and a uniformly consistent product is obtained. For example, in the manufacture of a rubber lid of a refrigerator cabinet, preforms $1\frac{1}{2}$ in. thick and having a weight of over four pounds each require 15 minutes in the press after being preheated. Without preheat a curing time of 45 minutes is necessary.

Rubber, loaded with carbon black, is a non-homogeneous mixture and local hot spots may be generated due to an uneven dispersion of the carbon black, but because of the relatively long curing cycle which follows the preheat, temperature differences are evened out and uniform curing ensues.

14.3 MOISTURE EXTRACTION

The evaporation of one pound of water by radio-frequency heating requires from three-quarters to one kWh of R.F. power, according to the material processed and the design of the drying oven. The cost, therefore, of removing large quantities of water from an inexpensive commodity is generally uneconomical, but when the material is temperature sensitive or the end product valuable, and the percentage of moisture to be removed is small, dielectric heating has great possibilities.

Although it must give way to conventional methods used for the artificial drying of timber in bulk, it can be used for drying small batches of selected woods for special purposes, i.e., lead pencils, musical instruments, etc. It is of great value too in removing moisture from materials which are in bulk or package form.

The principle of uniform heating obviates the risk of overheating the outside as is so liable to occur with other methods. It also gives a control over the rate of evaporation, which is not practicable with any other method of drying. For example, the moisture content of tobacco delivered in bulk may be high and variable between consignments. Before packing for distribution it must be reduced to a standard low figure, be uniform and not vary between deliveries. Dielectric heating fulfils these conditions.

14.4 TEXTILE INDUSTRY

In the textile industry, yarns and single layers of fabric are dried readily and economically by steam-heated convection driers, but when the yarn becomes a 'cheese' or bobbin, convection drying is extremely slow.

The plant occupies large floor space. The drying time may be several hours or days, and even then the moisture content of individual cheeses may vary by as much as 8 per cent. To obtain uniformity it is common practice to dry beyond the point required and then allow the yarn to regain moisture in a conditioning room.

When R.F. heating methods are used, the time is reduced to a half-an-hour or less, and the cheeses are dried uniformly to a predetermined moisture level.

Moist materials absorb R.F. power more quickly than dry ones, consequently when the time cycle and power input is controlled, batches of the same material having variable moisture content may be dried to a uniform level.

14.5 CERAMIC INDUSTRY

In the ceramic field there are advantages in drying quickly the unfired biscuit for heavy porcelain parts for the electrical industry,

Fig. 154. Food processing – continuous drying oven. The product passes freely underneath the electrodes. High-speed dielectric heating units of this type can be installed in food factories for other purposes such as sterilising, deinfesting, or re-heating of foodstuffs.

and for thick refractory crucibles which under normal air-drying conditions must stand for days before they can be fired. Floor space in the drying shed is reduced considerably, and climatic variations in the atmosphere are avoided. So far pilot plants only have been installed.

Very few solids can be reduced to 'bone-dryness' in contact with air and consequently vacuum drying has often to be used where the material has to be finished to a very low moisture content. Dielectric heating permits this to be done quicker and with larger masses without the use of vacuum plant. The heating which takes place in the body of the material increases the vapour tension and the mobility of the liquid so that it can move more freely through the material to the surface, from which it can be evaporated easily without the need for a high temperature.

In the chemical industry many temperature-sensitive and inflammable compounds contain unwanted moisture which is difficult and sometimes impossible to remove by conventional methods. In such cases dielectric heating can be helpful.

14.6 FOOD PRODUCTS

The processing of food products—as distinct from heating and cooking—involves the removal of moisture. Most food products are temperature sensitive and bulk processing involving the partial or complete removal of moisture is extremely critical. Dielectric heating can be used for the purpose; moisture is extracted rapidly, and the degree of drying is under control. Normally the drying of starch-reduced rolls after baking and before despatch takes some two or three days in an air-conditioned room, but the time may be reduced to 30 seconds when dielectric heating is used.

Figure 154 shows a drying conveyor upon which the rolls are tipped directly out of the baking oven. The equipment illustrated (with side panels removed for photographic purposes) develops heat within the starch-reduced rolls, and is capable of removing up to 50 lb. of moisture per hour with an R.F. input of 18 kW.

Many problems have yet to be solved, however, in the application of dielectric heating to the processing of food products, and there is ample room for experimental work in this field. Some applications have proved to be impracticable and uneconomical, but others warrant further investigation.

14.7 STERILISING AND DE-INFESTING

Dielectric heating can be used for sterilising dried and packaged materials such as flour, grain and plant bulbs.

An exposure of about 30 seconds can be sufficient to destroy all insect life, including eggs.

A conveyor type of unit would be suitable for these purposes.

14.8 DIELECTRIC HEATING IN COMBINATION WITH OTHER HEATING METHODS

Heat processing by conventional means involves the transfer of heat by convection, conduction or radiation, or by a simultaneous operation of all three modes, and a fruitful field of experimental work lies in the use of dielectric heating as complementary to one or all of them.

For example, it has been noted that the cost of removing large quantities of water from an inexpensive commodity, by dielectric methods, is generally uneconomical. If, however, the latent heat of evaporation is supplied by conventional means and the dielectric heater is only called upon to supply the sensible heat to remove deep-seated moisture, a substantial reduction of drying times is obtained, with increased production at slight extra cost.

Glossary
of technical terms
as used in industrial high frequency heating

Note : These terms are extracted from the Standard Glossary of Terms, B.S.2759 : 1956 published by the British Standards Institution.

GENERATORS

Generator. Apparatus for converting electrical or mechanical energy into electrical energy at the required frequency.

Valve Generator. A generator in which energy is converted to radio frequency energy by means of a high vacuum (or hard) thermionic valve in conjunction with an oscillatory or tuned *tank circuit.*

Spark-Gap Generator. A generator in which a capacitor, charged to a high voltage from a mains-frequency transformer, is allowed to discharge into an oscillatory circuit by the breakdown of a spark-gap. The process is repeated, and successive trains of damped h.f. oscillations are thereby generated.

Output Transformer. A transformer connected between an h.f. generator and a heating inductor. In the case of a valve generator, the primary winding is usually a part or the whole of the generator tank inductance.

In some cases, the output transformer is an integral part of the valve generator. In others, it forms an entirely separate unit (see B.S. 1799, ' Power rating of valve-driven high frequency induction heating equipment ').

APPLICATION EQUIPMENT
INDUCTION HEATING

Workpiece (Work). The piece or part to be heated.
NOTE. The term ' workpiece ' is applied particularly to heat treatment, brazing, etc.

Charge. The piece or part to be heated.
NOTE. The term ' charge ' is used especially for material to be melted in an induction furnace.

Heating Inductor (Work Coil Applicator). A conductor, usually water-cooled, arranged to carry h.f. current and to induce current in a *charge, workpiece* or *load* for the purpose of generating heat therein.

Surface Heating. The heating of the surface of a *workpiece* by means of induced h.f. currents in a surface layer.

Through Heating. Heating by induction methods of the entire volume of a *charge* or *workpiece*.

NOTE. When induction heating is used, the interior is heated by conduction of heat from the surface layer. The permissible power is limited by the thermal diffusivity of the material and the required degree of uniformity of temperature from surface to interior.

Coreless Induction Furnace. An induction furnace in which the heat is generated directly in the charge, or in the crucible containing the charge, by means of a coil surrounding it and in which the magnetic flux is generated without the use of a closed magnetic circuit.

NOTE. This definition distinguishes coreless induction furnaces from melting furnaces, commonly used on mains frequency, in which a loop of molten metal is linked with a closed ferro-magnetic circuit.

Submerged Heating. Heating which takes place while the *workpiece* is submerged in quenching liquid.

Workhead Transformer. An output transformer, not forming an integral part of the generator, which is mounted close to the work, whereas the generator to which it is connected is some distance away.

Quench Ring. A device in the form of a ring having orifices or jets through which the quenching fluid is sprayed at the appropriate moment on the area to be hardened.

Self Quench. A method of quenching in which the cooling of a heated layer is effected by the rapid conduction of heat into the cold core.

Single-Shot Treatment. Heating where the heat is applied continuously, though not necessarily at a constant level, for a prescribed period, the total area being raised to the temperature required in a single operation.

Progressive Treatment (Scanning). Heating where the *workpiece* is moved relatively to the heating inductor, in such a manner that the workpiece is progressively heated.

Skin Effect. The concentration of alternating current in the surface layer of a conductor.

Penetration Depth. The nominal depth below the surface of a conductor within which current is concentrated owing to skin effect.

Hardened Layer Depth. The depth to which a steel *workpiece* is hardened by means of h.f. heat treatment.

DIELECTRIC HEATING

Electrodes. In dielectric heating. The metal plates or other devices for applying the electric field to the material to be heated.

Transverse Heating. Of laminated material. A form of dielectric heating in which the electrodes are so positioned that the electric field is perpendicular to the layers.

Longitudinal Heating. Of laminated material. A form of dielectric heating in which the electrodes are so positioned that the electric field is parallel to the layers.

Glueline Heating. A specific form of longitudinal heating relating to the heating and setting of glue films. It is a term widely used in the wood-working industry.

Stray Field Heating. A method in which heat is developed in regions outside the space immediately between the electrodes.

Spot Glueing. A method of applying heat to a glued assembly, in which the glue is made to set in spots that are more or less regularly distributed.

Seam Welding. A process, using dielectric heating, for uniting thermoplastic material by softening and pressing the parts together along a prescribed line.

GENERAL TERMS

High Frequency Heating (H.F. Heating). A general term covering the whole field of industrial induction and dielectric heating by an alternating field of a frequency above mains frequency.

Loss Factor. The product of the power factor and the relative permittivity of a material. The heat generated in such a material in a given alternating electric field is proportional to this loss factor.

Screen (Shield). An enclosure of metal sheet or mesh for reducing stray electrical or magnetic fields.

Index

Printed in Great Britain by King & Jarrett Ltd, London, S.E.1.